SO SUE ME

BLACKWATER PRESS

First published in Ireland in 2014

Blackwater Press Ltd.

1–5 North Frederick Street, Dublin 1

© Suzanne Jackson, 2014

ISBN: 978-1-909974-04-3

The author and publisher wish to thank Evan Doherty Photography (https://www.facebook.com/evandohertyphotography), Ami McPartlin hair stylist, Michelle Regazzoli make-up artist and Laura Mullett (www.lauramullett.com) stylist for their assistance with shooting and styling many of the looks featured in this publication. Thank you to Life Style Sports, River Island and Om Diva for supplying many of the pieces featured in the shoot for this book.

We gratefully acknowledge Emma Kenny and Tara McCauley for the illustrations featured in this publication.

Additional images supplied by Brian McEvoy and Rachael Graham.

Printed in the Republic of Ireland

Contents

Acknowledgments

To my Mum and Dad – there are no words to thank you both for everything! You are both my rock and I love you both so much.

To my Publisher John O'Connor – thank you with all of my heart for making my dream a reality once again. You are a true gentleman and I love the friendship that we now have, your stories always brighten my day. Thanks also to the editorial team at Blackwater Press and Liz White, my designer.

Tara King – my back bone in this book! Thank you so much for all your time, ideas, opinions and advice! Without you this book just wouldn't be possible!

Dylan – my boyfriend, my rock, my everything, you are the best person I know. Thank you for photographing our NYC trip, (which I know was stressful) and for offering your fitness advice in this book! I love you.

To my SoSueMe.ie contributors – Dave, Sam and Michelle – still to this day – none of this would be possible without you guys! I'm so happy to call you my friends and I love the fact that you have grown with me and SoSueMe.ie! I appreciate your time and I will forever cherish your support and encouragement! Go team SoSueMe!

To my book contributors:

Illustrations

Emma Kenny and Tara McCauley. Thank you for taking the time out to draw the beautiful illustrations that feature throughout my book. You are both extremely talented. Emma, I love the pictures for the beginning of each chapter – you have a wonderful design imagination and I wish you the best of luck with your new website www.emkillustrations.com, no doubt your new journey will be a huge success!

Styling

Laura Mullett – THANK you for styling my book photo shoot you are one of the most professional and hard-working girls I know and you captured my fashion style perfectly.

Photography

Evan Doherty thank you for the pictures in book 2. I know I can always rely on you to get the job done and done well.

Hair

Ami McPartlin – you know big hair and I want to thank you for taking the time out to style my hair for this book, you nailed every look!

Make-up

Michelle Regazzoli – thank you for doing my make-up, you are a perfectionist.

To all my family and friends – you have all supported me in many different ways, but most of all, thank you for believing in me.

Lastly but by no means least – thank you, the readers! You made book number one a success and I'm back with another thanks to you guys. I hope you enjoy it just as much as the first... I have certainly bared more in this one :)! You all encourage and inspire me to keep doing what I'm doing.

I appreciate every single one of you! And remember, dreams do come true if you work hard enough! :)

Suzanne
xxx

Dedication

This book is for anyone with a
dream, an idea, or a plan to build
something from nothing.

Go for it and
don't look back!

Chapter One

Highs, Heels and How I Spent My Year

Dreams really do come true...

✿✿✿✿✿✿✿✿✿✿✿✿✿✿✿✿✿✿✿✿✿

FIVE YEARS AGO, I was made redundant from an amazing job. Suddenly I was broke and I was forced to take a small, part-time position that had no future and no prospects. To say my mood was at its lowest is a complete understatement! But one wet Wednesday afternoon, following much thought, I Googled 'blog templates', and so began the journey that would change my life! I am living proof that a risk, followed by plenty of hard work and persistence, pays off!

Even I can't quite believe just how much my life has changed. I was a part-time office manager when I first set up my blog, and now here I am, over 1.1 million readers per month later, sitting in a Starbucks in New York City, writing a chapter for my second book and uploading pictures from my time at New York Fashion Week! The past year has been surreal ... phenomenal ... actually, to be honest, there is no word that can completely sum it up. Literally SO MUCH has happened in the twelve months since my last book.

Suzanne

So What Happened Next?

The Bestseller

I think the overall highlight was signing a book deal with my publisher, Blackwater Press, and then going on to have my very own best-selling book: *SoSueMe – Secrets to Blogging, Fashion & Beauty*. I never in a million years would have guessed it would sell in the volumes that it did! It spent six weeks on the bestsellers list, making it one of the Christmas bestsellers! It was such a proud moment for me. I was never the brightest at school and yet there I was, a best-selling author! Even a year on, I still can't quite believe it, but it just goes to show, if you work hard enough and have faith in your dreams, life will surprise you in ways you never thought possible.

With my book on launch night!

With my sisters Katie and Carla

Signing in Eason, Galway

My first styling slot

With my sister Carla and my Dad Damian

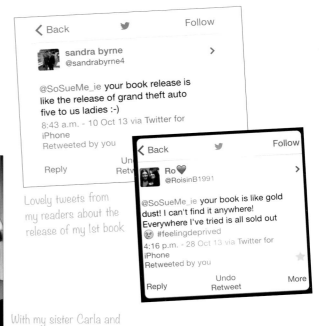

< Back   Follow

sandra byrne
@sandrabyrne4   >

@SoSueMe_ie your book release is like the release of grand theft auto five to us ladies :-)
8:43 a.m. - 10 Oct 13 via Twitter for iPhone
Retweeted by you

Reply

Lovely tweets from my readers about the release of my 1st book

< Back   Follow

Ro 🖤
@RoisinB1991   >

@SoSueMe_ie your book is like gold dust! I can't find it anywhere! Everywhere I've tried is all sold out
#feelingdeprived
4:16 p.m. - 28 Oct 13 via Twitter for iPhone
Retweeted by you

Reply   Undo Retweet   More

Breaking Into TV

My leap into television followed not long after the book. I was offered a number of styling slots on TV3's breakfast show, Ireland AM, and since then I have been offered a regular spot on the entertainment show *Xposé*!

Brushing Up

I also became the official ambassador for Crown Brush UK. My role with Crown Brush was my first ambassador role and it was genuinely a huge turning point for me. They are a massive UK company, and I had been such a huge fan of their products long before they approached me. I fell hopelessly in love with their contouring palette and used it so much that I figured I would record a YouTube video demonstrating my contouring routine, as it was something I was frequently asked about. The video was a huge hit, and Crown Brush completely sold out of the palettes as a result. It was following this that I was asked to be an ambassador.

Working as Brand Ambassador for Crown Brush

Style Awards

2014 was a year of contests and nomination lists! First I was voted one of Ireland's Top 5 Stylish Women in *RSVP Magazine*, and then I heard that I was nominated for the title of Most Stylish Newcomer at the VIP Style Awards. Unfortunately I didn't get to attend the awards ceremony on the night, but I was so delighted to be on their shortlist of nominees. The VIPs have been taking place for years now, and are a very established social event so I was absolutely thrilled to have received a nomination. Back when the 2013 list of nominees was announced, I remember saying to my friends, "Well, maybe I'll be nominated next year!" The power of positive thinking!

A clip from *RSVP magazine*

Ireland's Sexiest Woman

During the year, I was also voted Ireland's Sexiest Woman by readers of *The Sunday World* newspaper. No way did I expect to win that one! My boyfriend was equally as shocked as he thinks I look rough in the morning! Cheers Dyl!

The *Sunday World* feature on Ireland's Sexiest Woman

Milestones

Another highlight for me this year was when the number of fans on the SoSueMe.ie Facebook page officially reached six figures – 100,000! In fact, when my first book was released, it was like a double celebration because the 100k milestone had occurred around that same time! The page is now speeding towards 200k, which I'm very excited about. I am also hugely excited that the website, SoSueMe.ie, reached a new record of 1.1m readers in September.

SoSueMe.ie Workshops

I have been travelling a lot this year. When I wasn't flying back and forth from London, I was making my way around Ireland holding SoSueMe.ie workshops in various counties. The workshops were a huge success and I am still getting requests from readers to hold one in their county!

Meeting Mollie

I'm a total home bird by nature, but I have to say I do love travelling to London! Earlier this year, Oasis invited me over to London to have dinner with Mollie King from The Saturdays, as she had just launched a fab collection in conjunction with the brand. Mollie was so lovely to speak to; a real girly girl.

Queen Bey

I also got to see Beyoncé live in concert (OMG, Lady Yoncé is UNREAL!) Myself and three others were guests of Viviscal, the brand responsible for those fab hair supplements, and they brought us to London for an exclusive Viviscal media event that was also attended by lots of UK magazine editors. Afterwards, we were whisked over to see Beyoncé Live at the O2 right from our very own VIP suite! It was just so cool. We were transported to the O2 in cable cars. Honestly, breezing across London looking down at all the bright city lights beneath us was almost as amazing an experience as the concert itself!

SoSueMe.ie Workshop on Tour

Having dinner with Mollie King

At the O2 with Aisling from U mag

5

NYC

A major highlight for me this year was visiting the states for the very first time. I attended New York Fashion Week as a guest of Canon, and I also got to visit the apartment of a certain Miss Bradshaw... oh my God, the whole trip was incredible, but I'm going to save all the juicy gossip on that for the last chapter!

Official Adults!

Speaking of milestones, Dylan and I celebrated our two year anniversary in June, and we also moved in together last November! (Aghhh, we're officially adults, Dyl!) We have two babies... of the canine kind! Our first was a gorgeous Maltese dog, called Coco, and later, we took in another beautiful Maltese called Harper. I always miss them like crazy when I'm away.

In NY

Stellar magazine came to visit when we moved into our new home

Magnum Blogger

Last April, Magnum flew me out to London to document their 25th birthday party as their official blogger. To mark the occasion, they asked renowned designer, Henry Holland, to create a bespoke gown that resembled Magnum chocolate. (It looked un-buh-leevable!) The whole experience was incredible – very glitzy and so very fab – and as part of my role as Magnum's official blogger, I got to interview Henry Holland himself and record a video for Magnum in which I reported on the whole party.

I loved every second of it. Celebrities were as frequent a sighting as the bottles of champagne, and with it being Magnum's party, the glamour was off-the-scale! At one point during the party, I just stood for a brief moment, looked at the glamour around me and thought 'wow'. After all, it wasn't that long ago that I was sitting behind the office manager desk in 98FM, fielding calls, taking notes for people, and blogging whenever I had a couple of minutes to spare. Back then I was worried about my future because I had no idea what I wanted to do with my life. Once I set a goal and got to work on it, however, everything completely changed for me. You see, I work so hard and am always setting higher and higher goals, that I sometimes fail to really take things in when they're actually happening. My mind is always buzzing with ideas, plans I want to work on, meetings I have to prepare for, and topics I want to blog about. That night at the Magnum party though, I took it all in and realised just how unbelievably fortunate I am to be doing something I love so much.

With Henry Holland

Featuring in *RSVP Magazine*

Every day is crazy busy but so wonderful, and I don't think I have ever been happier than I am right now. Look, as cheesy as this is going to sound, there is no other way of saying it... SoSueMe.ie would be nothing without the readers and I am so thankful to each and every person who drops by the site, even if they only end up there by accident! Seriously though, without the readers, there would be no SoSueMe.ie.

I can't thank you enough for all your fab emails, not to mention your lovely messages and comments on Facebook, Instagram and Twitter. I'm not kidding when I say that they mean so much to me. Just recently, for instance, I had a right horror of a day. It was one of those days that was so unbearable, it would be enough to convince a lifelong pioneer to open up the liquor cabinet and pour himself a whiskey! Well, instead I opened up my emails, and one of them was from a SoSueMe.ie reader. I swear to God, her message made my day. That one email alone managed to turn my totally horrific day into a positive one. She told me about how much SoSueMe.ie had helped her, especially when it came to regaining her confidence. Immediately, it reminded me of why I do what I do. SoSueMe.ie is more than just a beauty and fashion blog; it's about helping people to find their inner-confidence and feel sexy.

My column in *Xposé* Magazine

It's not medicine, it's not changing the world, but you know what, if it helps brighten even one person's life, then I'm happy! Some people read the posts for entertainment, some read them for inspiration. I don't mind what reasons people have for reading as long as they get some enjoyment or benefit. I want this book to have the same impact.

In between the covers of this book, you will find everything from business advice, to life lessons, to guidelines on how to get that self-confidence burning within you. There will also be a sprinkle of beauty and fashion thrown in for good measure too. Well, it wouldn't be SoSueMe.ie without those things!

As with the first book, I don't want you to keep this one in pristine condition either. I want you to circle the parts you can relate to, underline the parts you want to remember, keep it on your dressing table or bedside locker and look to it whenever you need a spark of inspiration, motivation or encouragement. I want you to make good use of it.

I'm a tea lover, so Barry's sent me this

Don't just read the words, take heed of them! At the end of each chapter I have included a page for you to write down your own hopes, goals and highlights and make this book your own.

Before you start your journey through this book, get rid of any fears or concerns you have about your future. Whoever said people are supposed to have their shit together by the time they turn 30 clearly was not aware of the millions of opportunities in the world! I'm turning 30 this year, and I feel as though I only found my feet in the past twelve months.

This book requires a 100% positive mindset and a go-getting attitude.

Life is about to get exciting.

Your Highlights

Fab holiday with your pals? New job? Learned to drive?
Or finally found your perfect shade of foundation?

Write it down and read it back on those days when you need
a little pick-me-up!

....
....
....
....
....
....
....
....
....
....
....
....
....
....
....
....
....
....
....
....
....

Chapter Two

Live, Laugh and Lessons: SoSueMe's Guide to Life

I have job hopped a bit in the past. Actually, I have job hopped a lot! Waitress, promotions girl, shop assistant, office manager, model... you name it, I've worn the uniform. Not too long ago, I posted the following picture-quote on the SoSueMe.ie Instagram and Facebook pages:

"Nothing screws up your twenties more than thinking you're supposed to have your life together!"

Between Facebook and Instagram, the picture got thousands of likes and shares. It seemed to strike a chord with people but I can completely understand why.

People in their twenties are so worried. They think that they have to have their careers and lives fully sorted out before they hit 30, but the truth is, they don't.

I am now on the cusp of 30, not engaged, not on the property ladder, but do I regret anything? Not a thing! Would I change anything I did in my twenties? Not a chance!

I never knew what I wanted to do with my life when I was growing up, and to be honest, I really feel like I have only found my feet in the past year or so.

When I was in my last year at school, and all my classmates were eagerly discussing the CAO forms and colleges, I remember being majorly unsure of my future. That said, I didn't panic over this uncertainty. I always had a gut feeling that things would work out and that I would get 'there' eventually, wherever 'there' might be!

I talked lots about my early life in my first book, but here's a little recap for those who haven't read it. When I left school, I did a PLC course in Social Care. I hated it, but I stuck it out for the first year because I didn't want to be the only one of my friends not attending college. In the end, I completely flunked the first year exams. Granted, I hadn't been enjoying the course, but I was still upset that I had failed it. I ended up spending a few weeks lying in bed, depressed about the way things had turned out.

Following some encouragement from my mum, I went out and looked for a job. I ended up working as a shop assistant in Topshop, which I absolutely loved. One day, when I was on changing room duty, I noticed a girl arrive into the shop dressed head-to-toe in a fab looking Coogan Bergin uniform. I didn't know what Coogan Bergin was so I struck up a conversation with her, and asked her about it. She explained it was the college where she was studying beauty therapy and she then went on to tell me about the course and how much she loved it. The whole thing sounded incredible, and, as she was talking about it, I remember thinking about how much I would love to do something similar.

> "There are no mistakes, only opportunities"
> Tina Fey

Something about it struck a chord with me and I felt excited by the prospect of studying that subject. I discussed it with my parents and together we looked at all the different beauty therapy courses available. In the end, the reviews of Coogan Bergin impressed us most, so I opted to go there. The course was so tough, and very science-based, but I loved it so much. I really threw myself into it, and when exam time rolled around, I received all honours.

I had set my sights on working in The Haven, which was THE beauty salon back then. I knew I would get there at some point because whenever I put my mind to something, I always see it through. Sure enough, the moment I passed my exams, I knocked on their door and was employed on a trial basis, which subsequently led to a permanent position. I ended up working there for three years.

While The Haven was undoubtedly one of the best places I worked, there came a point where I wanted to move on. During my time there, I had become the top seller, the most booked-out beautician, and I had basically achieved all I could. I needed a new challenge, so I began looking through different job vacancies online, trying to figure out which area I would like to get into. When I read the job spec for 'recruitment consultant', it seemed very sales-orientated, and I knew I had the personality and the skills for the job.

It might seem crazy that a beauty therapist would apply for a recruitment job, but I figured there was no harm in taking the risk. I knew I had the skill to succeed as a recruiter, all I had to do was convince my interviewer. The first interview went so badly, but that didn't deter me. Eventually, I was called for an interview with Top People Recruitment. During the interview, I outlined all the skills I had acquired from my previous careers, and explained how I could apply them to a recruitment role.

In the end, they took a chance on me and offered me the job. It was such an amazing position. Top People was the kind of place where achievements were always acknowledged, and hard work was openly appreciated. This is what motivated the staff to set higher and higher goals for themselves. I became one of the most successful consultants within the firm, and I ended up working there for around three years. Although I loved the work, I felt like I had learned all I could with Top People. That longing for a new challenge was beginning to set in again. It was at that stage that I applied for the job of HR consultant with Hibernian. I remember thinking there was no way I would get the job, because they were looking for very experienced people with HR qualifications, which I didn't have.

In the end, I went through four interviews and was offered the job! I was probably the least experienced of the candidates who applied, but, I genuinely think it comes down to having the neck to go for something. I had convinced myself that I was perfect for the job. That's how I always approach new challenges. Even if I don't really believe I can do something, I will convince myself that I can, and then just go for it. I also make sure that I prepare intensely.

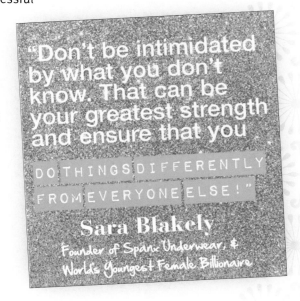

"Don't be intimidated by what you don't know. That can be your greatest strength and ensure that you DO THINGS DIFFERENTLY FROM EVERYONE ELSE!"

Sara Blakely
Founder of Spanx Underwear, & World's Youngest Female Billionaire

When I told my boss in Top People that I had been offered the job with Hibernian, they returned with an offer of an increased salary and commission stake, as well a number of additional incentives. They were determined to keep me there, and, because I loved them, I stayed. But shortly afterwards, the recession hit and I was made redundant from the recruitment industry. I had gone from enjoying a high-powered position with an amazing salary and lots of perks, to suddenly being unemployed, and living on social welfare for eight months. I hated that period of my life, absolutely hated it. I felt so depressed, and overall, it was a very low time for me. There's a lot to be said for just having a job to get up for in the morning. I went back online searching for vacancies; I was determined to return to employment.

Eventually, I underwent an interview with the CEOs of Spin1038 and 98FM, and was given the position of part-time office manager.

I'll admit I wasn't overly excited by it, but I kept reminding myself that it would expose me to the media industry. That was undoubtedly the silver lining. Little did I know then that it would change my life! With the heavy celeb traffic passing my desk, I figured I could write a blog from the perspective of a normal girl working on a reception desk.

I started putting a plan together. My friend and I brainstormed ideas, and even though we came up with a number of names, none of them stood out quite as much as SoSueMe.ie! I remember being so determined to find a name that people would remember. I wanted to create a potential brand name, and SoSueMe.ie just seemed perfect!

When I look back on my life, I can see how everything led to me being where I am now. I have never been happier, but I would never have made it here had I not been made redundant. Losing my job felt like end of the world for me, but now I see that it was actually the beginning of an incredible journey. So stop pressuring yourself to 'have your life together'. Enjoy your twenties, that's what they are there for. Make mistakes, fall in love, fall out with friends, make new friends, travel, do whatever you want, it's your life!

> "Don't wait for extraordinary opportunities. Seize common occasions & make them great. Weak men wait for opportunities; strong men make them."
>
> Orison Swett Marden

Before my big 3-0 arrives, I have been thinking about what I have learned over the past few years; the kind of things I wish someone had told me a few years ago! So here is my advice to you, the things I wish I could tell my eighteen-year-old self!

1. Leave your comfort zone

If you want access to the endless opportunities in the world, then you have to step outside your comfort zone. It's scary but it's one of the most rewarding things you will ever do. After all, you can't shine if you are always hiding away in the shadows of your fears. You have to face what frightens you, and embrace every opportunity with open arms. Once you do this, good things will start coming your way.

2. Happiness lies in the small things

This is something I have only fully realised in the past year or two. I always thought that happiness lay in money, career, and a stylish social circle, but it doesn't. I have five pairs of Louboutins in my wardrobe and they don't make me any happier than I was when I had none. Yes, I look at them with pride, because they were bought with money I worked hard to earn, so I do see them as a reflection of accomplishment, but they don't make me any happier. I know this might sound cringey but real happiness for me comes from the little things in life, like my dogs Coco and Harper, going for lunch with my parents, having our own apartment, having my own little business, and having a wonderful relationship with my boyfriend Dylan.

I had never been in such a loving, rewarding relationship before. I had been cheated on in the past, but now I feel totally secure, and there is no material thing that can equal that feeling.

At home with Dylan

3. Be patient

It has often been said that you can't rush something if you want it to last forever. This is especially true when it comes to the areas of career and fame. Too many girls expect to be successful and/or famous almost immediately, but it doesn't happen like that, and I can guarantee you if it does, it won't last. The truth of the matter is if you want to make your life amazing, then you are just going to have to work harder than everyone else.

4. Give it everything you've got

This is something I tell everyone who attends my workshops. Always give your 100%. Whether it's a job, a relationship or a friendship, don't let something slip from you without having given it everything you've got. For example, if your last relationship turned out to be a bad one or if you were cheated on, then don't let there be a wall between you and the next person that comes into your life.

5. Enjoy your accomplishments

In the past I was always setting goals, always looking for the next big thing, so I never really stood still for long enough to appreciate what I had achieved. Some ladies would throw a party if they had a book on the bestseller list or if they had been voted Ireland's Sexiest Woman by readers of a national newspaper, but I never celebrated those things because I was always looking for the next challenge. What I have learned, however, is that you have to be happy with what you already have while you are striving to achieve more.

My best-selling book

6. It's okay to not know everything!

When I first started blogging, I hadn't a clue. I didn't even know any bloggers. The thing is, I was passionate about beauty and fashion, and that's why I succeeded. I loved what I was doing. If you are knowledgeable about a subject and have the belief that you can excel, then I say go for it. You'll make mistakes but you will also learn along the way. If you're passionate about what you do and open to the possibilities, then it can only go one way!

7. You can learn from heartbreak

Having your heart broken is like a rite of passage into adulthood. Every girl has experienced it, every girl has been hurt by it, but you know what? Every girl gets over it! I have been in love three times; I have been cheated on and have had my heart ripped to shreds, but those experiences taught me some valuable things about myself. Getting over your first heartbreak makes you strong. The next relationship I was in after that, I figured well if this doesn't work out, I know I'll be able to handle it! Hard times make you realise your own strength. On that note, never stay with a guy who doesn't realise how lucky he is to have you. There are plenty of guys out there who will look at you like you're magic, so never ever stay in a relationship that is making you unhappy. Know your self-worth, and know what you want. I had just come out of a relationship when I started SoSueMe.ie, and it helped me to be able to channel all my energies into the blog.

8. Have confidence

Confidence is not loud or arrogant. In fact, it's anything but. Real confidence is being who you are, wearing what you want, and saying what you want to say without feeling the need to apologise for it. I was never a confident girl. Yes, I was confident around friends and when talking to people, but when it came to my own inner-self esteem, I always lacked. It's only in the last year that I have realised if you don't have a strong sense of self-belief and self-confidence, you will be swallowed up by the world. I achieved a thick skin by putting myself out there, and learning to react differently to negative comments. I would try to find something constructive within a comment, and if I couldn't, well then I deleted it from both the site and my mind. Confidence is not something you can really explain, it's more of a feeling. This is why people tend to like being around those who exude confidence. They are who they are and the don't apologise for it.

9. Take risks

This is one of the most important life lessons I have learned. If you want to do something worthwhile, then you have to just go for it. I took a huge risk last year when I left a full-time job. I went from a guaranteed salary of €2,000 a month to not knowing if I was even going to make €200 the next month. I saved a good bit of money during the months prior to my resignation, so that I would have a financial cushion to fall back on in case the blogging didn't work out. If I hadn't taken that risk, SoSueMe.ie would not have blossomed as much as it did. Sometimes, you just need to take a big risk to really feel the pay off.

Working on SoSueMe.ie in the apartment – something that never would have been possible without taking a risk

10. Live for yourself

I used to care far too much about what people thought of me and what they said about me. I did everything I could to keep my ex-boyfriend happy, and I sacrificed a lot of friends along the way. I cared more for him than I did for myself. You can't always be trying to please someone else. You have to do what is right for yourself first. Those who genuinely care for you and love you will stick around, and those who don't can jog on! On that note, don't be afraid to stand up for yourself either. You're not a doormat, and don't allow anyone to treat you as such.

11. Leave the past in the past

I recently read a quote that went, 'people are never truly happy because they always believe that their past was better than their present and that their future won't be as good as their past'.

People always look back on the past as having been better than it was, but you can't move forward if you are preoccupied by way back when. Leave it behind you and you will change for the better.

12. Make mistakes

I have made plenty of mistakes, and I don't regret any of them. Mistakes are essential for character growth. They help you to learn and improve. They are also a sign that you're being innovative and taking risks. Just make sure you don't dwell on any mistakes, move on from them.

13. Stop searching for perfection

Stop chasing perfection, it doesn't exist. Learn to accept the things you consider to be your 'flaws'. When I was younger, the lads would slag me and call me a lanky streak because I was thin and scrawny, and for years I hated my shape. I wanted a curvier figure, but now that I'm a bit older, I'm so grateful that I'm naturally slim. I also used to hate the freckles on my arms. I covered them up and wouldn't dream of letting a guy see them. Now that I'm a bit older, I have completely accepted them. Remember, what you might consider to be a flaw, someone else considers to be beautiful.

14. Buy it!

Want something? Just buy it. If you really love it and you can afford it, then you won't regret it. I have walked away from many a handbag or pair of shoes, and I always end up kicking myself. Just buy it!

"Do your thing & don't care if they like it"
Tina Fey

15. College isn't everything

College is a wonderful opportunity but it's not for everyone. I know that my working life has given me more skills and experience than any college course ever could.

In the end, your exams will not determine your overall life path. Yes, education is important, but your attitude, work ethic, and mindset, are the three traits that will take you further than any degree could.

16. Don't be afraid to ask questions

I am always curious and am forever asking questions. If I don't understand what someone is talking about, I just ask them to explain it. So many people are often too embarrassed to ask questions for fear of looking stupid, but there is absolutely nothing wrong in asking for something to be explained. No one knows everything, and no one likes a person who pretends to either!

17. Be around people who encourage you

When I was working in Top People Recruitment, I was doing extremely well and so I didn't feel like a failure anymore. I remember having a chat with my colleague Nicki one day and throughout the course of the conversation I mentioned how worried I was that recruitment might not work out for me and questioned if my future lay in the HR industry. I don't think I will ever forget what Nicki said back to me. She said, 'Suzanne, what you touch turns to gold. You have the mental attitude needed to succeed. You're a hard worker and you will always find your feet.'

At the time, I remember thinking she was mad because I didn't know where I was going in life and here she was telling me I would succeed. Today, however, I can see exactly what she meant. I was always a positive, enthusiastic person, and I think those traits shone through in any job I put my mind to. The environment I was working in also helped me considerably.

I also worked under a boss, Chris Doyle at 98FM, who used positive reinforcement. He motivated his staff and encouraged us to succeed by using bonuses and other perks. We knew our hard work would be recognised which is precisely why we worked so hard! If I had worked under a boss who belittled and discouraged me, I wouldn't have stayed in that company, let alone succeeded there. When encouraged and reassured, people thrive.

18. Remember things could always be worse

No matter what happens, things could always be worse. In a year's time, you won't even remember what you were stressing about today, and if you do remember, you'll wonder why it stressed you in the first place. If you have your health, you are richer than you think.

> "When you focus on problems, you will have more problems.
>
> When you focus on **POSSIBILITIES**, you will have more **OPPORTUNITIES**."
>
> ~ Unknown

19. You don't know what someone is going through

This is very true! You can't judge people by what they post on their Facebook and Instagram pages. I can tell you right now my life is not as glam as it looks on social media. I still have my own problems, my own shitty days, and my own worries. What you see on social media are the highlights. Think before you comment on someone's page, regardless of who they are. You don't know the half of what the other person might be going through so if you have nothing good to say, then say nothing.

Never forget social media's golden rule. Don't post anything online that you wouldn't be happy to have printed on the front page of a national newspaper with your name beside it.

20. Laugh a lot... then laugh some more!

I went through a really hard time last year when I was on holidays. I was getting so many hater comments and the whole thing really upset me. That night, I went out to a club with a couple of friends, and while we were out, we bumped into a guy we knew. He's just the funniest guy ever. I laughed so much that night that my stomach was actually sore by the time the night was over! Despite having had the most awful day, I felt so wonderful that night. Laughing with friends is the best cure for the blues, undoubtedly.

The lessons you've just read through represent the things I learned as I grew up and tackled all the things in life that came at me. I hope that they can be of use to you and save you some awkward learning curves. But I know that it's not easy to just read advice and act on it. I'm not here to lecture. You need to have your own experiences in order to grow as a person. However, I do know that life is a lot easier when you can approach each day with confidence, so next up I'm going to tell you how I learned to walk tall and meet each challenge that came my way.

Life Lessons

What have your experiences taught you?
Put your life lessons down on paper and create
your own collection of words to live by.

....
....
....
....
....
....
....
....
....
....
....
....
....
....
....
....
....
....
....
....
....

> "The critical ingredient is getting off your butt and doing something. It's as simple as that. A lot of people have ideas, but there are few who decide to do something about them now. Not tomorrow. Not next week. But today. The true entrepreneur is a doer, not a dreamer."
> **Nolan Bushnell**
> American Entrepreneur

Chapter Three

Have No Fear:
SoSueMe's Pep Talk for Success

PEOPLE TEND TO associate confidence with things like power dressing, a purposeful stride, a firm handshake, good posture, and so on. Yes, confidence may look like all of these things, but true confidence is a state of mind, and in order to acquire it, you must first start visualising exactly the kind of person you want to be. You say you want to be confident, but in what way? Do you want to walk into a room full of people on your own? For some, that doesn't sound like much of a challenge, but to a lot of people, it is the most daunting one imaginable. A common problem is speaking in front of a crowd, but perhaps you would just like to have enough confidence to speak to one person without feeling nervous or tongue tied? Whatever it is you want to achieve, visualise yourself doing it.

Visualise every detail, from how you present yourself (shoulders back, head up), to how you walk (tall, and like a lady with a purpose), and even the tone you use when speaking (firm but polite). The more accurate the image, the better. Now here's the important part. As you go through the visualisation, feel the confidence fire up inside you. In order for the visualisation to be successful, you have to actually experience the feelings that go with it too.

Your subconscious cannot tell the difference between what is real and what is imaginary, so if you are able to visualise a more confident you, then you will be able to make it a reality.

Model yourself on a confident person you admire. Observe their behaviour and mimic it. Whenever Kate Middleton goes for a jog through a park, or goes shopping in her local supermarket, you can be sure all eyes are on her. But, rather than feel self-conscious in trainers and minimal makeup, she always acts as though no one is even looking at her and carries on doing her own thing. Despite constantly having several long lenses focused on her by photographers hell-bent on capturing an unflattering shot, she treats the outside attention as though it doesn't even exist. In many cases, confidence is being aware of the attention, but not reacting to it. Yes I know it's easy for Kate Middleton to be confident, because let's face it, she's Kate Middleton, but she wasn't born into royalty. She was an ordinary girl who had no choice but to develop the confidence to deal with the sudden media attention her then-boyfriend brought with him. If she can do it, there's no reason why you can't.

In order to become more confident, you must stop giving a damn about what people think of you. You will never be confident or successful if you allow the opinions of others to control your life. Confidence is centred around self-belief. Now, when I say self-belief, I don't mean vanity or arrogance, I mean being so secure in your own skin that you are practically bullet proof, or even bully proof! It's easier said than done, I admit, but you cannot allow people to bring you down, and you absolutely cannot allow the comments of others to dictate your mood. You need to get into the habit of sending critical words in one ear and out the other. The best way to do this is to work tirelessly on improving your mindset. Achieving success and confidence lies in the type of messages being delivered to your sub-conscious mind. So what are you constantly telling yourself, and is it of a positive or a negative nature?

Hypnosis is quite a good place to start with this. As I mentioned in my first book, I underwent hypnosis sessions in the famous Golden Hypnotherapy Clinic to help me deal with the bullying I was encountering online. It worked wonders for me, but if a one-on-one hypnotherapy session is out of your budget range, then look into purchasing some hypnosis CDs or MP3s. Glenn Harrold and Ailsa Frank are two very established individuals in the field of hypnotherapy and they both have hypnosis CDs and MP3s that can really help adjust your thinking and boost your confidence.

You should also try to read everything you can about how your mindset affects your life. The more you understand, the more you will be able to change for the better. *The Secret* is a world famous bestseller and definitely one of my own personal favourite books, however another international bestseller I would recommend is *The Power of the Subconscious Mind* by Dr Joseph Murphy. From around the second chapter onwards, it will totally help you change the way you think.

If you feel like you lack in confidence or are painfully shy, the one thing you need to remember is that it won't last forever. You are not stuck with it, and it's not who you are. The reality is this: no one stays the same. Who you are now, is not who you will be in five years' time. I myself am a very different person at 30 compared to the one I was at 25! As I said in the last chapter, it's only in the past year that I feel like I really found my feet. The past twelve months have made me more confident in myself, and I do feel as though I have grown a lot as a person. If you make an effort to improve your mindset, who's to say that you too won't be a far more confident person this time next year?

My Own Story of Finding The Confidence & Keeping It!

THROUGHOUT MY TEENS and for most of my twenties, I did not have a clue as to what I wanted to do with my life or where I wanted to go. I always knew I wanted to be in business, I just didn't know what type. You know how some girls grow up knowing what they want to be? Well, I wasn't one of them! What my twenties has taught me however is that you will always end up where you are meant to end up. I was a hard worker, and I always have been, but I never did particularly well in school. I got around 300 points in my Leaving Cert, although I probably could have done much better if I had studied a little harder. That said, even when I did study hard, I was never an A-grade student. I hated Maths, absolutely hated it! I just couldn't grasp the subject. I barely managed a pass in my Leaving Cert, and I remember being convinced I was going to fail it. I also found it difficult to grasp language subjects, which I suppose wasn't helped by my dyslexia. I always did the best I could though, and that's why I have pretty much zero regrets about school. There isn't anything I would change about the path I chose.

You see, regardless of what I was doing, I always worked insanely hard. I made good connections wherever I could, but most importantly of all, I listened to my gut instinct. Whenever I was unhappy in a particular place, I either looked for the silver lining or I got out of it. When I was working as an office manager in a radio station, I was pretty miserable because I felt like I wasn't going anywhere. Instead of wallowing in my misery however, I decided to take advantage of the steady stream of celebrity traffic passing my desk each day, and so, I started the SoSueMe.ie blog. Richard Branson was right, there are opportunities to be found everywhere you go. Blogging began as a hobby, but over a number of years, I developed it into a business. Yes that's right, it took a number of years! Some people expect immediate success when they set up a blog, but that never happens!

I never went to business school, and I never did a business course of any sort. Everything I have learned has been as a result of my own experiences, but I think this made me a stronger person overall. It certainly made a businesswoman out of me. When you're passionate about something, you focus more on the job rather than the results, and this makes a huge difference. That said, things didn't always go to plan for me.

When you get into business, be it any kind at all, you have to be strong enough not to allow the setbacks to set you back. There will be occasions where people will disappoint you, betray you, screw you over, and let you down, but don't allow these experiences to taint your outlook. Instead view those situations as learning experiences and move on, grateful to be a little bit wiser.

Perseverance and Self-Belief

MY MOTTO HAS always been 'work like a boss'. Even back in the days when SoSueMe.ie was a hobby, I approached it like a boss would a business. A good sense of self-belief will carry you through times of rejection, helping you to power on with the same enthusiasm you had when you first started. You are going to make mistakes, or make decisions that you might later regret but you cannot spend too much time on the past or it will distract you from where you are going in the future. I took a big risk when giving up my job with 98FM to go blogging full-time. The security of a job was of course tempting, but the idea of having my own business was far more enticing. I also figured that the regret of giving up on a dream would far outweigh the regret of giving up a job.

I'm sure there was a moment or two when Bill Gates could have kicked himself for having dropped out of Harvard to pursue the failed venture, Traf-O-Data. If he did, he certainly didn't dwell too long on it, nor did he beat himself up about his situation. He had the self-confidence to know he would hit success at some point, so he got right back down to hard work and eventually created a business called Microsoft! You may not have success with your first blog or business, but this is why perseverance is so important. Those who become the most successful are those who take responsibility for their lives and careers. They decide they are going to be as successful as is humanly possible. They don't rely on luck; they make their own. They set goals that most people would consider crazy, and even though they might silently agree that their dreams are outrageous, they will still go right ahead and make them a reality anyway! They take action, but they also react positively when their action is thwarted by something like rejection.

I love reading about the business figures who went on to enjoy phenomenal success after having experienced constant rejection, because it reinforces my own belief that anything can be achieved through hard work and perseverance. If it were not for perseverance alone, we wouldn't have brands like Starbucks or Disney. It's hard to believe, but some of the best-known brands in the world were knocked back hundreds of times over before they had even begun. You cannot let rejection knock you back. Ever. If you have sufficient self-belief, a strong work ethic, and are willing to persevere, then very little can stop you. After all, there are few things fiercer than a ballsy businesswoman!

If you take anything away from this chapter, remember this – stop being so hard on yourself, live in the moment and try to understand that no matter how you feel, your emotions are temporary... Life is a gift and you have to live it.

I will now leave you with these two mantras that I love and stand by:

1. Never sell yourself short on someone who puts a question mark over you.

2. 'Trust me, it's paradise. This is where the hungry come to feed. For mine is a generation that circles the globe and searches for something we haven't tried before. So never refuse an invitation, never resist the unfamiliar, never fail to be polite and never outstay the welcome. Just keep your mind open and suck in the experience. And if it hurts, you know what? It's probably worth it.

   You hope, and you dream. But you never believe that something's gonna happen for you. Not like it does in the movies. And when it actually does, you want it to feel different, more visceral, more real.

   And me, I still believe in paradise. But now at least I know it's not some place you can look for, 'cause it's not where you go. It's how you feel for a moment in your life when you're a part of something, and if you find that moment... it lasts forever...'

Personal Manifesto

Maybe you don't yet know what you want to do or where you want to go. But who you're going to be is up to you. This page is for your dreams... and your plans for achieving them!

....
....
....
....
....
....
....
....
....
....
....
....
....
....
....
....
....
....
....
....
....
....
....

Chapter Four

#LikeABoss:
SoSueMe's Guide to Business

❋❋❋❋❋❋❋❋❋❋❋❋❋

Have the confidence to take as many chances as you can in life. Forget the past and resolve right now to stop blaming your parents or your circumstances for where you are. Take responsibility for your life and work hard. The reality is that your dream career/life/body/relationship is going to require lots of perseverance, self-discipline, and dedication.

Success is a journey and it won't be a plain sailing one either. You're going to endure plenty of set-backs, and you're going to hear the word 'no' so often that you'll wonder if the whole world is determined to keep you from succeeding.

"If people are doubting how far you'll go, go so far that you can't hear them anymore."
Michele Ruiz
Entrepreneur

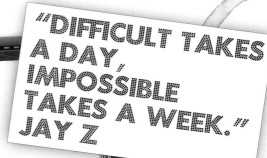

YOU'RE GOING TO have plenty of people slam the proverbial door in your face, but here's the thing. Every rejection is character defining, and makes you that bit stronger. It's a cliché, but it's true. When I was made redundant, it felt like the end of the world, but now I look back and realise that if it hadn't happened, SoSueMe.ie would never have happened!

So, are you going to be the type of person who takes no for an answer, or are you are going to be the type who breaks down the door when the window of opportunity seems bolted shut? Yes, there is a possibility your idea might not work out, but did you ever think of how wonderful it would feel if you did succeed? I have a great admiration for the ballsy risk takers, the ones who decide 'to hell with this' and just go for it. Granted, there is a big difference between being a risk taker and being reckless, and I am most definitely not advocating the latter! It goes without saying that you must do plenty of research before running with an idea.

One business woman I greatly admire is Sara Blakely, the founder of the famous Spanx Control Underwear. Her persistence, hard work, and determination, has resulted in her becoming the world's youngest self-made billionaire. She has a brilliant quote that goes, 'Don't worry about what you don't know – it could help you change the game'. She's right! Too often, people are held back from pursuing their ambitions of starting their own businesses, because they focus on all the things they don't know about rather than concentrating on what they do know. You can't allow your dreams to be stifled by doubters, not even the ones inside your own head! In the grand scheme of things, your success in life will not be based on Leaving Cert points, but rather hard work, attitude and ambition.

Remember that!

Rules for Being a Ballsy Businesswoman

Don't think big, think huge.

If you pair this mindset with a good attitude and an admirable work ethic, then you are already well on track towards making your dreams come true. You have to put something out there to get something back. Never quit! You're further ahead than you think.

Visualise yourself achieving your dreams.

When I first set up my blog, I didn't ever consider the idea that it would fail. If anything, I imagined it being huge. The blog wasn't even online at that point but I still visualised it being a huge brand in years to come. When I was trying to think of a name for the blog, I remember my goal was to create a name that people would remember. Now, I wasn't naïve by any means; I knew there was a chance that it might not take off. After all, there were no big-time Irish blogs back then, but even still, I envisioned mine being a big success. I asked myself, 'Well, WHAT IF my little blog one day becomes a business?' This is why I was determined to give it a name that stood out.

Think of power and confidence as being nothing more than states of mind.

Even the most successful business figureheads have silently doubted themselves and their abilities at some point, but they never respond by cowering in a corner or shying away from a task. Even if a project terrifies them, they go ahead and do it anyway. They get things done. Spanx founder Sara Blakely used to suffer with crippling anxiety when it came to public speaking engagements. She stuck with it, though. In fact, to get herself pumped up and ready for action before going on stage, she would listen to the Eminem track 'Lose Yourself'. I often doubted what I was doing. When I first started out, I was scared what people thought of me. This worry was reinforced after some girl wrote a scathing post about me on a showbiz site telling people to 'check out Suzanne Jackson's blog for all your deluded needs'. She even went on to say quite a few nasty things about me. It was a very personal attack. I bet you a pound a penny that she herself currently blogs, trying to make it work for her, but nothing would work for anyone with a nasty steak like that in them.

Read up on people who have been hugely successful in your field.

Study their traits and habits, and try to apply them to your own life. The one common factor you will find amongst all successful people, regardless of the industry they are in, is that they are supremely hard workers. Even the ones hailed as 'overnight successes' invested hundreds of hours and made an abundance of sacrifices to get to where they are today. Stop expecting

immediate success and recognition. You won't get it until you have worked for it. Take last summer for example. I spent those long sunny(ish) days at the kitchen table writing chapters for my first book. From June until September, while all my friends were attending BBQs and drinks events, I was strapped to my desk, writing and editing. Even when all my friends were out enjoying the 12 pubs last year, I was in bed early ahead of my book signing session in Limerick the following day. Anyone who wants to be ultra-successful will have to make sacrifices along the way. If you are not willing to sacrifice part of your social life to work on your dream, then you have to ask yourself, how badly do you want success?

Don't be afraid to be a rule breaker.

Some of the most successful people in the world are famous for their love of breaking the rules. Sam Walton, founder of the world famous Wal-Mart chain, wrote in his autobiography that the number one rule in business is to break all the rules. He wrote, 'I always prided myself on breaking everybody else's rules, and I always favoured the mavericks who challenged my rules'. I always knew deep in my heart that I wanted to be my own boss. I always worked hard for employers, but I challenged their decisions and I spoke up for myself if I felt something in the workplace wasn't fair. I would break the rules from time to time too. A lot of my bosses really liked me and I think it's because I was fun, outspoken and not afraid to break the rules. Remember, you can invent your own rules. That is a trait of a ballsy boss lady!

Erase the term 'someday' from your vocabulary.

You have everything you need to get started right now. You really do! There is always a way to get your foot in the door. Want to run your own shop? Well, start by setting up an eBay shop or a Depop account. This will give you sufficient time to save money for a retail premises of your own. If I had waited for 'tomorrow' to set up SoSueMe.ie, then it probably would never have materialised, or even be where it is now. When I think back, I started at just the right time. The market wasn't flooded with blogs, and blogging itself was a relatively new concept. This gave me ample time to find my feet and make the sort of mistakes new bloggers wouldn't get away with today, like crap layout, over-posting and typos.

It's true what they say. If you're dreams don't scare and excite you, then they're not big enough.

Prior to the release of my first book, I was terrified. I don't think I had ever felt nerves like it before! Similarly, when I attended London Fashion Week for the first time, I felt so alone and scared because I was at this huge event by myself, surrounded by all these industry heavyweights. That feeling of nervous excitement is vital; it's what keeps you going when times get tough. I remember how anxious I was before I met Marc Jacobs in London for our interview. Of course this wasn't helped by hiccups like our plane taking off late due to bad weather! That trip from the airport to the venue was one mad rush, and when I got there, the nerves multiplied. The thing is, what starts off as nerves tends to turn into adrenaline and excitement somewhere along the line. In my experience, if a project scares you, it's worth seeing through!

At London Fashion Week

Know what you're talking about.

If you can't explain something in simple terms, then you don't understand it well enough. This is a great guideline to take everywhere with you, especially in business. Simplicity always wins out in the end.

But don't pretend to know it all.

No one respects, or wants to do business with, a know-it-all! Everyone has their strengths and weaknesses, and the best thing you could possibly do is find someone who excels in the areas in which you are weakest. If crunching numbers is your Achilles' heel, then find a programme that takes care of accounting tasks, or outsource the job to a professional. Personally, I dislike administration and I'm disorganised so I joined a management agency to help me organise my time, my work, accounts, etc.

Don't waste time with comparison.

Compete with yourself, not others. Judge yourself on your personal best and you will accomplish anything you put you mind to. Remember that while someone else might currently be more successful than you, they too were once where you are right now. No one starts off at the top.

Don't be afraid to ask questions.

How else will you learn? Ask plenty of them, and do so with confidence. To this day, I still ask people/professionals questions. If I don't understand something, I won't hesitate to ask that person to explain it further. It's okay not to understand something the first time around. Personally, I love learning from people and asking as many questions as I can. It's the best way to grow.

"Life is short. Don't be lazy."
Sophia Amoruso

Show respect to people regardless of their job title.

I know from first hand experience how much of an impact respect can have. I had been working in 98FM for about a year when I met the station owner, business tycoon Denis O'Brien. He was in the station to meet with top management but on his way out, he stopped at the reception desk and started chatting to me. Now, when you are working behind the reception desk, as I was at the time, most people will just breeze by you without even glancing in your direction. Denis O'Brien, however, as I discovered that day, was not like 'most people'. He sat down, and for twenty minutes he chatted to me about everything and anything. He asked me about myself, my family, where I was from... I couldn't believe it. He is one of the most successful businessmen in the country but yet he didn't think himself too big or too good to sit down and talk to the office staff and take a genuine interest in what we were doing. You just knew he appreciated everyone associated with his business. Ever since that day, I have had the ultimate respect for Denis O'Brien. The point I am trying to make is, don't be an asshole to the people who might not have the best job. Respect works on all levels.

'If someone offers you something, and you don't know how to do it, take it, and learn how to do it.'

I can't remember where I first heard that advice, but it has stood to me well. My first slot on the TV3 entertainment programme *Xposé* came about after my agent Jules phoned me one evening and asked if I would be free to do an *Xposé* style slot the following morning in the Liffey Valley Shopping Centre. I froze. I had never done a style slot like that before and the time frame seemed way too narrow to make it a success. I told her that there was no way I could do it; I needed more time to prepare. Her reply was simple. She said I was going to accept the opportunity and go through with it as it was the only way I would learn the ropes. I was so scared and overwhelmed (no really, I genuinely had no a clue what I was doing) but I knew Jules was right, so I raced out to the Liffey Valley Shopping Centre, pulled the stock I needed, went home and prepared for the slot. I was back in Liffey Valley early the following morning for the *Xposé* recording. It all went brilliantly and afterwards I wondered why I had been so scared. Ever since then, I have promised myself that whenever a daunting opportunity arises, I will grab it without question and then figure out how to successfully see it through. Being thrown into the deep end will very often produce the best results!

Your gut feeling is always right.

If you have a bad feeling about something or someone, trust it and move on. My gut instinct has never failed me. I trust my instinct and it always tells me the right thing to do – all those jobs I left, the windy path I took, my cheating ex – I knew deep down each time something wasn't right.

Street Style Photo shoot.

Recording a YouTube video for the SoSueMe.ie channel.

No matter how many times I do it, packing for a business trip to London is always stressful!

Book signing in Eason.

The Life Of A Blogger

THE LIFE OF a blogger is manic. This is why I try to be as healthy as possible. There's no room in my life for fatigue or dipping energy levels. When I was writing this book, I took a little look back through the pages of my trusted pink Filofax. One particular week involved several business meetings, an appointment with my publisher to sign off on my first book, attending events, writing blog posts for SoSueMe.ie, filming for TV, and flying out to London for the Cosmo Blog Awards! After arriving back in Dublin from the Cosmo awards very late one night, I was again up bright and early the following morning to film a blogger segment for RTÉ. Once that was wrapped up, I was on my way to Athlone where I spent a number of hours giving out styling and fashion advice in Athlone Town Centre. It was non-stop, but would you believe, that was probably a quiet week by comparison to other weeks in my schedule!

When I say blogging is a 24/7 job, I really mean it. Even when I was away on my anniversary break with Dylan, I was making and taking calls, writing, sending emails and carrying out a PR photo call for my SoSueMe.ie workshop in the G Hotel in Galway. When people are enjoying a Sunday lie in, I'm usually up writing blog posts on my MacBook, or penning a chapter for my book, or just sorting through my schedule for the coming week. I give my everything to SoSueMe.ie because I love it. In order to continue doing what I do, however, I can't let myself burn out, so I always make sure I set aside some time to relax. I won't lie, I do sometimes find it difficult to completely switch off at first because I am so used to being busy and on the go all the time, but I do treasure my quiet time with Dylan where I can just chill out and turn off my phone. Earlier this year, we spent a night in the Seafield Golf & Spa Hotel in Wexford and honestly, that one break away helped me so much. I was able to return to work refreshed, revived and ready to take on anything.

As busy as I am, I wouldn't change my career for the world. I love what I do and I am blessed to be doing it.

Press photo call for my Galway workshop in the G Hotel.

Giving a fashion talk in Athlone Town Centre.

I had just finished up my book signing in Eason Galway here, and was about to race on to my next work appointment! Even on the weekend, us bloggers are busy!

A blogger's job is never over! Working while holidaying in Egypt.

Presenting an event for SEVENTEEN Makeup.

Behind the scenes at a photo shoot for The Dress Pantry.

An everlasting love affair between a blogger and her iPhone!

Making an appearance on TV3's Midday Show.

In the air again! Flying to London.

Hosting a style talk in Blanchardstown Shopping Centre.

THE SOSUEME BUSINESS MANIFESTO

Believe in your idea **Enthusiasm is everything**

Don't listen to the doubters Make mistakes

Learn from your mistakes Take risks

listen Ditch your fear of failure Network

Speak confidently **Make contacts** Take a chance

Blaze a trail forward dream huge

be ballsy Create your own opportunities

Make things happen don't ask for permission

Read Look for inspiration everywhere

Create your own future **Don't procrastinate**

Don't be afraid to say no **Work hard**

Drop all fears Every problem has a solution

Always stay ambitious **Do it!!!**

Set the bar high & never give up

#PlanLikeADreamer
#WorkLikeABoss

> "The fastest way to kill your creative voice is to start worrying what other people are going to think about what you wrote"
>
> Author, Karen Rowe
> www.karenrowe.com

YOU WILL ALWAYS know a goal-setter when you meet one. They're the ones with an ambitious fire about them, a big dream and an even bigger plan. They're the ones with the fearless gene, the positive outlook, and the work ethic to rival that of any CEO you see on the pages of Forbes! They don't coast along, they go out and make things happen. They discuss ideas and possibilities. They create opportunities, and rarely will they allow a setback to actually set them back! Instead they leap forward and take responsibility for their life, and they sure as hell make it as exciting as they can! They are the types of people you want to be around because their infectious enthusiasm makes you feel as though you can achieve whatever you put your mind to. In their world, anything is absolutely possible. And what's more, they're absolutely right!

Writing out your goals, even just one, can give you the motivation you need to make the changes you need! It's not enough to just think about your goals, you have to write them out and decide on the steps you are going to then take. There's nothing more exhilarating than having a goal you are passionate about and seeing it through to the end. If you have a drive to achieve something, you will automatically work harder to get it. Each step you take closer to your goal gives your life an element of excitement. If however you have no plans, no goals and are just living month to month, then where is the fun in that? Where is the challenge? The bigger the goals, the scarier they are, but you know what? Goals should scare you! They should scare the crap out of you... and when they do, then take it as a sign to dive straight in and make them a reality!

Every January, I sit down and write out a list of goals I want to achieve during the coming year. I'm not going to tell you about all of my goals, because I haven't achieved them some of them yet, but over the following pages you can read about the ones I have achieved.

SoSueMe's 2014 Goals

"Create my own brush line"

I will be releasing a ten piece collection of makeup brushes — The SoSueMe Collection — in conjunction with Crown Brush. This limited edition collection will consist of my ten favourite brushes that I know every girl would get plenty of use out of. Too often, a brush set will consist of a few brushes that you will never use, and not enough of the ones you would use, so I decided to create the ultimate set!

"Create a SoSueMe app"

I didn't go with the app in the end, because I didn't want to take traffic away from the SoSueMe.ie website. When I looked into it, I realised it didn't make good business sense so instead I made SoSueMe.ie mobile responsive. That way, it's easier for readers to browse the site on their phones or tablets.

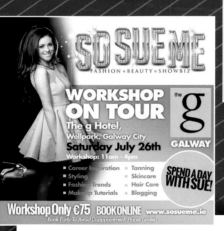

"Start SoSueMe master classes"

I started my workshop master classes in March 2014, and each one completely sold out! I had only intended to do four, Galway, Dublin, Belfast and Cork, but the demand is now such that I will be taking them to even more counties! They will be continuing all throughout next year.

"Travel to New York and document my whole trip!"

When I wrote out this goal, I had no idea that my second book was going ahead, nor did I have any inkling that I would be invited to New York Fashion Week! Both came as a huge surprise! In the end, I got to travel to New York and document my experience for my book!

"Get my lash line back on track"

Last year taught me a lot about business. It taught me a lesson in getting back on track when things don't go as planned. Last Christmas you might remember that I was on the verge of releasing a range of SoSueMe strip lashes. Everything was good to go. The products were ready, the packaging was perfect, the lashes themselves were amazing, and then... crash. At the last minute, for reasons that I can't go into, the whole project fell through. That taught me to always be prepared to deal with the crap hitting the fan. Not everything will run smoothly, and sometimes, like in my case, the people you are depending on will let you down. I was so upset and disheartened by how that project had turned out because I had invested so much time and work in making sure the final product was absolutely perfect. I'd had a specific vision of an amazing product and I had worked hard to make it a reality. There was also a matter of my professional pride being on the line. I had already told fans about the products, and I had even written about the lashes in my first book. I had no reason to keep it a secret. The products were practically ready for the shops. Anyway, when the venture went to dust, it provided me with a good learning experience, so rather than cursing my bad luck and dwelling on the negative, I picked myself up and went looking for a new business partner. I started over afresh, and as a result, the SoSueMe line of strip lashes will be released this year instead!

New York

"Bring out another book"

I didn't think this would happen because I honestly didn't think I had another book in me, but here we are! Once I sat down and started writing, I realised I had more than enough for a second book. Sometimes a goal can seem so intimidating, but once you get to work on it, it becomes manageable and you realise your own potential.

"You will not do incredible things...

... without an incredible dream!"
John Eliot

As you can see from my goals, I listed the things I wanted to achieve whether they seemed possible or not, even if they were going to be hard work, and then I figured out how to get there. And sometimes pure luck helped me out!

Try to find one thing you can work towards in your personal life, business life, etc.

Write your goal on an A4 sheet of paper, and then work out the steps you would have to take in order to reach that goal. Make a pact with yourself right now that this time next year, you will look back on the previous twelve months with a sense of pride and accomplishment.

Secrets To Blogging Success

In my first book, I explained how to set up a blog and attract readers. If you persisted with your site and posted regularly, then chances are, you have built up a loyal readership. Now you just need to concentrate on taking your blog to the next level. To help you do this, I have outlined a number of guidelines that will enable you to expand your fan following, thus resulting in a more popular and hopefully profitable blog. If, on the other hand, you're still struggling with your blog since you set it up, don't worry! The guidelines listed over the next few pages will also help you progress.

Building credibility

Integrity is a big thing with me! I firmly believe that a blog stands little chance of success unless it has built up a strong sense of credibility. This goes for the blogger too! If I don't like a product, I won't write about it. Simple as! The purpose of the SoSueMe.ie beauty reviews is to inform my readers of the products I have tested and loved. If I find a small downside, then yes of course I will point it out, but if I completely dislike the product, then I just won't feature it on my blog. I am also careful about who I associate SoSueMe.ie with. Not too long ago, I was offered quite a large sum of money to represent a hair care brand, but their products are of such low quality that there is no way I would associate SoSueMe.ie with them. The way I see it, my blog is a reflection of me, it always has been and always will be. I am 100% honest with my readers and that's precisely why a product tends to sell out whenever I recommend it. My readers know I am genuine and not plugging something in exchange for a cheque.

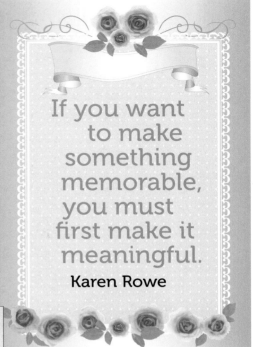

If you want to make something memorable, you must first make it meaningful.
Karen Rowe

Testing a product

Business cards

Even during the early days, I brought my business cards everywhere with me. It gave an edge of professionalism to my role as a blogger, especially back then when blogging was relatively unheard of. It also ensured that new contacts would remember the name SoSueMe.ie. If you are serious about your blog, then business cards are absolutely essential. After all, where is the sense in networking if no one knows how to contact you afterwards, or worse, no one remembers you? These days business cards are an inexpensive purchase, but they are hugely effective. You can design your own business cards online, but make sure the design is absolutely spot on before you even think of handing them out to anyone. Show some draft copies to your most honest friends and actively look for feedback. Always remember, the card represents the personality of your blog, so you have to ask yourself, does it do it justice? For instance, if your blog centres around subjects of a political nature, then it makes no sense to choose fluorescent colours and floral borders, when instead you should be opting for a design that conveys a more serious tone.

43

Email

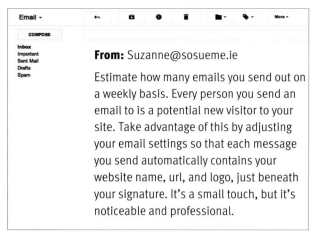

From: Suzanne@sosueme.ie

Estimate how many emails you send out on a weekly basis. Every person you send an email to is a potential new visitor to your site. Take advantage of this by adjusting your email settings so that each message you send automatically contains your website name, url, and logo, just beneath your signature. It's a small touch, but it's noticeable and professional.

#Spammers

Too many spam comments on either a blog or a Facebook page delivers just one message: neglect. Most blogging platforms, like WordPress, automatically detect and block spam, but if a few manage to sneak through the filter, make sure you delete, delete, delete! Readers who pop by your site may want to engage with you and others who comment. They won't be enticed to do so, however, if they have to wade through messages plugging pills designed to cure everything from sunburn to baldness! The same goes for your Facebook page. Spam comments are downright annoying and their presence gives the impression that the owner of the page is not looking at the comments. On this note, make every attempt you can to reply to questions or comments left on your blog or Facebook page. Granted, the bigger your site becomes, the more difficult this will be, I know this only too well, but do make a solid effort. I get so many emails and comments every day that it would literally be impossible to reply to every single one and still have the time to blog and carry out day-to-day SoSueMe.ie business. I do make a massive effort to reply to as many as I can, and readers openly appreciate this.

Put yourself out there

To be a truly successful blogger, you have to have a balanced mix of Go-getter, Networker, and Promoter. These are the three crucial traits you will need to make your venture successful. Be honest with yourself and identify which areas you could improve upon. Are you in regular contact with PR companies? Do the PR people even know you? If not, send them an email or give them a call to introduce yourself and ask to be placed on their mailing list. Remember that you are representing your brand, so always show respect to the people you're dealing with and don't ever be pushy. No one owes you anything. If a PR agency doesn't reply to an email, then send a polite follow up, but don't get moody about it. Moody might work for Anna Wintour, but that's only because she's Anna Wintour!

How often do you post?

If you are hoping that your blog will eventually become a business, then you have to treat it like a job you love, rather than just a hobby. I know this sounds obvious, but you wouldn't believe the amount of bloggers who only post when they feel like it. You don't only go to work when you feel like it, so don't approach your blog with that attitude. You need to be consistent and post regularly otherwise you will never stand a chance of growing your readership. Successfully turning a blog into a business is an extremely difficult feat, and one achieved by a very select few. If you want to be one of that few, then you have to be prepared to put yourself out there and work extremely hard. During the early days, it can be quite difficult to invest time and effort in creating posts, when you can't be sure even one person will read them, but hey, you can't reach one million readers, without first reaching just one! When producing content, do so as if you have a massive audience waiting eagerly for your next post. When SoSueMe.ie began, I had just one reader. It meant a lot to me to even have that one reader and the excitement of knowing that someone was reading my content actually made me determined to grow my readership. Don't make the fatal mistake of telling yourself that you will start working hard on your blog when you have a large audience. The reality is this: if you don't work hard in the early days, your blog will never have a large audience.

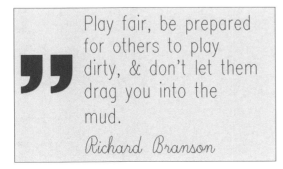

> Play fair, be prepared for others to play dirty, & don't let them drag you into the mud.
> *Richard Branson*

Promoting yourself and your blog

If you're really serious about elevating your blog or website to dream-like levels of success, then you definitely can't be shy when it comes to promoting it. When SoSueMe.ie was one year old, I used this early milestone to my advantage and threw a party to mark it. I invited lots of media people along, and as a result, pictures from the event made it into the newspapers and social websites. I also had SoSueMe.ie birthday banners around the venue which ensured that the logo and name could be seen in the majority of photographs snapped on the night. I handed out gift bags and SoSueMe.ie cupcakes to the guests in attendance. Anything I could attach the SoSueMe.ie logo to, I did! The blog was a hobby at the time, but I always approached it as though it were a business. I worked my ass off, and that hasn't changed! Of course, I didn't realise at the time that it would actually become a business for me, never mind a full-time one! Even though this was only a couple of years ago, it was still pretty unheard of for someone to blog at a professional level. I suppose I loved working on SoSueMe.ie so much that it came naturally to me to want to push the name out there as much as I could. What I'm saying is, you always have to be on the lookout for opportunities to grow and promote your blog. Maybe you could throw a party like I did when SoSueMe.ie was a year old? Anything that draws positive attention to your blog will help you acquire new readers.

> "I'm a big believer in persistence, not being greedy, and, above all, working hard." Caprice xoxo

Expertise is a process

This might sound insanely obvious, but I'm going to say it anyway ... never stop learning about the industry you're blogging about. You might think you know everything there is to know, but you don't! Even if your blog falls into a tiny niche, I guarantee there are advances taking place and as a blogger, you need to be aware of these. Anyone can set up a blog, but not everyone can enjoy readership figures that contain as many digits as a telephone number, so what sets you apart? Expertise. I enjoy going to the movies, but I'm not going to set up a movie review blog because it's not an area I would be very knowledgeable about. In order to build up a strong readership, you must position yourself as an expert in your field. You can only do this by being on the ball and knowing your subject better than your fellow bloggers do.

Handling the critics

THE DREAM OF being successful goes hand in hand with the nightmare of being a target for haters and internet trolls. In my first book, *Secrets to Blogging, Fashion & Beauty*, I spoke about my encounters with haters, and the response I received was pretty overwhelming. Many readers identified with what I was going through, while others were shocked to learn about the other side of what they thought was a very glamorous life and business.

If you shun the average 9 to 5 lifestyle in a bid to follow your dream, then you are inevitably going to draw attention to yourself, and the fact of the matter is that sometimes the attention will be negative, though perhaps not at full-blown hater-level! I can't stress enough how important it is to have confidence in yourself and your business. If everyone else is doubting and criticising you, you will need to be able to stand firm and continue on regardless, and only self-belief will help you do this.

Of course, understanding the motivation behind a person's comment or opinion will help you distinguish between those who are critical and those who are concerned. For instance, your family might try to discourage you because they want to protect you from getting hurt, which is totally understandable. After all, my mum was worried when I first started SoSueMe.ie. I had taken a loan to get the site up and running, and she didn't want to see me spend money on a venture that might not go anywhere. She was just being a naturally protective mother with her daughter's best interests at heart.

Other people however might try to discourage you because they don't want to see you succeed. I don't know why anyone would hate to see another person do well; it's a mindset I will never understand. Maybe it's basic jealousy, or maybe it's because one person's success highlights another person's insecurities when it comes to pursuing their own dreams. Whatever the reason, these are the vipers to be wary of.

Many critics will argue that they are just sharing an opinion, but there's a fine line between an opinion and a veiled insult. It's not okay to type out every comment on your mind. They way I see it, if something I say doesn't make someone's day better, then I won't say it.

It's almost inevitable that when you are dealing with haters, you will find yourself thinking, 'what if I packed it all in right now?'

I have certainly experienced those horrible days where the haters seem to be on a never-ending quest to kill my enthusiasm and love for blogging. On more than one occasion, I have had fleeting thoughts about how peaceful a life I would have if I just gave it all up. If I cut the cord on SoSueMe.ie, sure, I wouldn't have to deal with nasty vitriolic comments, nor would I have to deal with trolls constantly criticising every detail of my appearance, from the length of my hair to the size of my waist! On the other hand, however, I also wouldn't have the beautiful emails and messages from the readers who tell me about how much they love reading my blog every day and how they were inspired by my story. In the end, the positives will always outweigh the negatives. Whenever you find yourself dwelling more on the bad than the good, you need to ask yourself what's more important: the happiness of you and those who love what you do, or, the happiness of the haters and internet trolls who would love nothing more than to see you give up?

When I Grow Up...

❀❀❀❀❀❀❀❀❀❀❀❀❀❀❀❀❀❀❀❀❀❀❀❀❀❀❀❀❀❀❀❀❀

Maybe you haven't yet started your first job, or maybe you're working but you don't yet have your dream career. Here's where you spill out all those thoughts about things you know you could be good at, and start to plan the future...

Chapter Five

Eat, Sleep, Train, Repeat:
SoSueMe's Guide to Fitness

FITNESS IS EQUALLY as beneficial for the health of your mind as it is for the health of your body. When you get into a routine of exercising, even if it's only a brisk walk or a cycle each day, you get addicted to that feel-good factor that comes with it. If you combine regular exercise with a healthy meal plan, you will notice an improvement in your mood, your energy levels and your quality of sleep too. When you think about it, there are no downsides to exercising regularly! I'm not perfect at this and nobody is. I just do my best and I still enjoy my Dominos and Malteser bars as little treats.

But for me, it's important to be fit because I am on the go so much. I really can't afford to be fatigued because I'm self-employed and run off my feet, so I always make sure I set aside some time for exercise. When I asked readers what they would like to see in the book, a lot of you asked if I would share everything about my fitness routine and my daily meal plan. If I shared everything, you'd be hearing about days when I skipped the gym and cheeky trips to Eddie Rockets… but here are some of the healthy routines I try to stick to that you might get some inspiration from. Just remember that this is what works for me, but everyone is different!

My Exercise Routine

Before I go any further, I just want to make it clear that I am not a fitness expert; that's Dylan's domain! I'm not saying my routine will work for everyone, I am merely just outlining the routine that I follow. Take from it what you will.

The core of my workout consists of three sets, with each set featuring three exercises. Remember, you have to carry out each exercise immediately after the last without any delay. The higher the intensity, the better.

Perform each exercise around ten or twelve times, as this is the optimum range for building muscle and burning fat. As you progress over the coming weeks and months, then you can increase that number, but the main thing is to start low and work your way up.

The Routine

If you carry out this routine twice a week, as well as attending a class or two, then you are well on your way to fitness success. Just make sure to take one or two days rest so as to let your body recover.

Set 1

* Squat with dumbbells into overhead press (x12)
* Mountain climbers (as many as you can for 20–25 seconds)
* Walking lunge (x6 each leg)

Repeat the set three times, resting for 60–90 seconds between each repeat.

Set 2

* Deadlifts (x12)
* Burpees (x12)
* Single armed rows (x12 each arm)

Repeat the set three times, resting for 60–90 seconds between each repeat.

Set 3

* Dumbbell chest press (x12)
* Dumbbell fly (x12)
* Press ups (x12)

Repeat the set three times, resting for 60-90 seconds between each repeat.

The three sets usually take around 30-35 minutes to complete. Afterwards, I do some abs exercises, such as crunches and planks. Everyone has different levels of capability when it comes to abs exercises, but a great starting point for the crunches would be to do around 10-20, while for the planks, it is recommended that you start off by holding the plank shape for about 20-30 seconds. Increase on both of these as the weeks progress.

The whole programme I have just taken you through is a high intensity full body workout. It's ideal for me because it targets all the main areas, while at the same time burning fat and building muscle. Pilates is another big favourite of mine. I always look forward to going to my Pilates class in Westwood Gym, because I know I will feel amazing by the time I leave. I love that the focus is never on any one individual in the class, and the only part of the room that is lit up is the stage, so no one feels self-conscious either. For a vigorous work out, I go to a BodyPump class. I also attend a spinning class, which is hugely beneficial because it is a very high intensity workout so it burns a lot of calories. It's also super fun and enjoyable. If you are looking for a class with a wonderful social aspect to it, then spinning is probably the one to go for.

Honestly, I don't like going to the gym by myself, which is why I like having Dylan as my personal trainer. He helps me stay motivated and keeps me firmly on track with my programme. He also ensures that I do all the exercises necessary for me to get the results I want.

For instance, when I'm in the gym, I especially like to concentrate on toning my legs and bum. Dylan therefore has me do various exercises such as squats, deadlifts, and lunges. These all target the relevant leg and bum muscles, thus helping me to achieve my goal. One of the main advantages of having a personal trainer is that you learn the proper techniques for each exercise. So many people are doing the exercises wrong, but a personal trainer won't allow that to happen.

I have to admit, I hate cardio, mainly because I don't find it challenging enough. The thought of spending an hour on a treadmill or a cross trainer bores the life out of me! I also know from Dylan that I will achieve far better results if I invest my time in high intensity exercises. If you carry out a high intensity workout for thirty minutes, you will burn way more calories in that half hour than you would if you went running at a steady pace on a treadmill for a full hour. The best part of a high intensity workout is that it also shoots up your metabolism so that your body continues burning calories in the hours after you have finished exercising.

An example of a high intensity workout would be High Intensity Interval Training. Sprint for 30 seconds, then take a rest until your heart is back to its rest rate, and then repeat the sprint again. Repeat this ten times, and you will burn a lot more calories than if you went running at a steady pace for a half an hour. You will be out of breath, so drink plenty of water during the rest period. Concentrate on your breathing too and get it back to a relatively normal pace before you sprint again.

If you want to be in better shape, then you have to educate yourself on nutrition and exercises. A beach body doesn't just happen. There really is no easy route. Once you get into your fitness routine though, you genuinely won't want to stop. I know I'm hooked on the feel good factor the exercises produce, and even though I might be tempted to skip a training session, I always remind myself of how good I will feel after it's done. That in itself is usually enough to get the motivation pumping.

To help you prepare for your fitness journey, I have asked Dylan, in his role as a personal trainer and fitness writer for SoSueMe.ie, to outline a couple of pointers that you guys should bear in mind.

Dylan's Tips

Use the camera not the scales

I receive so many emails from girls wondering why the number on their weighing scales has remained the same, or even increased when in fact they have been exercising relentlessly. It's not a nice shock to get, especially if you have been training so hard, but don't worry, it doesn't mean you are not losing weight.

The difference between fat and muscle is density. Muscle is far more dense than fat. To put it into context, imagine muscle and fat as being like a pound of oranges next to a pound of feathers. The oranges and feathers might weigh the same, but the feathers would take up more space. This is how fat works. Fat takes up around three or four times the space that muscle does, which is why it is possible to be slimmer but yet still weigh the same. If you have been training regularly, and notice that your scales have a higher reading, then take it as a good sign, because less body fat and more body muscle is how you acquire a healthy, toned figure. I would suggest that you ditch the scales immediately, as there are far more accurate ways to ascertain the results of your hard work. One of the best ways to gauge how much your body has changed for the better is to track your progress with pictures. Before you embark on your journey, take three full-length pictures of your body: one side picture, one front picture and one back picture.

Take new pictures every 4-6 weeks afterwards, and you will literally have a full clear view of any physical changes that have taken place. You will be able to visually track your progress. Another way to assess the improvements taking place is to look at how your clothes are fitting. Is there a bit more room along the waistline of those jeans perhaps? Is that t-shirt not as snug as it usually is? This is a great way to estimate how you are doing. If you are a member of a gym, ask for a body fat test. The device they use will accurately measure your body fat, as well as identify the areas that require further work. The point I am trying to make is that you should never rely on the scales for feedback. They are so misleading. After all, there are a variety of factors that can cause your weight to fluctuate a little. Things like water retention and time-of-the-month, all affect the reading shown on a weighing scales.

Don't be afraid of lifting weights

So many women are afraid of lifting weights, because they think it will make them bulky. I promise, you won't pile on bodybuilder-sized muscles as a result of lifting weights. Bodybuilders acquire their physique by training seven days a week over a number of years, and all while following a VERY strict meal plan. Women also don't produce the same amount of testosterone as men, which means it would actually be quite difficult for weight-lifting to yield very bulky results in a woman! The truth of the matter is that you burn more fat by lifting weights, so don't be afraid to use them. Weight-lifting exercises will leave you feeling stronger, fitter, as well as slimmer and more toned. Of course, it's not recommended that you just go into a gym and start lifting weights without prior knowledge of how to use them. There is an actual technique when it comes to weights. If you are a member of a gym, don't be afraid to ask one of the trainers there to show you how it's done. They're only too happy to help!

And finally ...

Don't obsess over weight loss. The point of adopting a healthy lifestyle is so that you can be fit, healthy and full of energy. Focus on those three factors, and the additional benefits, such as glowing skin, thick shiny hair, loss of excess fat, and better quality of sleep, will all automatically follow. Starving yourself will not give you that beach body you want. Depriving yourself of nutritious food will just leave you ill and very lethargic. Cutting out nasties such as sugar and wheat are what will lead you to optimum health and a fab figure to boot.

My Home Fitness Programme

IF THE GYM is not your thing, then don't fret. You don't need a ton of fancy gym equipment to get fit and toned, you just need to know which exercises are the most beneficial. Here, Dylan has compiled five essential home exercises that will target the main areas women regularly complain about. Whenever I don't have time to get to the gym, this is the routine I follow at home.

Exercise 1 – Burpees

Burpees work a number of muscles in the body, thus making them a fantastic addition to any routine. You will hate them at first, but trust me, they will give you results. Burpees also strengthen almost every major muscle in the body, and best of all, they will help increase your overall metabolic rate so that you burn calories faster. As burpees are so intense, even performing 10–20 consecutively can keep your metabolism going long after your workout.

To carry out a burpee, all you have to do is:

1	2	3	4
Start from a standing position, then lower into a squat position with your hands on the floor in front of you.	Kick your feet back so that you are now in the push up position.	Kick your feet forward again before returning to the start position.	Finish with a jump with your hands reaching over your head.

If you want to really challenge yourself, you can add a push up in the middle of the exercise.

Exercise 2 – Mountain Climbers

Like burpees, mountain climbers are also quite high intensity, but this makes them a wonderful exercise for burning fat. The steady running motion targets your glute and leg muscles, including your quadriceps and hamstrings. Improved balance and co-ordination are two additional benefits of this exercise.

Personally, I think mountain climbers are a great exercise for shedding any unwanted body fat, but it's vital that you learn how to correctly carry them out first.

To carry out a mountain climber, all you have to do is:

1

Get into the plank position. Your hands should be directly under your shoulders and shoulder-width apart. Your feet should be hip width apart, and keep your arms and legs straight. Keep your core tight and your back should be in a nice straight line with no arch.

2

Once you feel stable and in a nice athletic position, bring your right knee under your abdominal muscles and then return it to the plank position. Repeat this with your left side.

3

As you get more comfortable with the exercise, speed it up. Aim to do 20 on each leg when starting off.

Exercise 3 – Squats

If you want toned legs and bum, then I'm afraid you have no choice but to add squats to your fitness routine. Squats target a lot of different muscles, such as your glutes, quadriceps, hamstrings, and calves, so even though you will find them quite tough at first, the main thing to remember is that your hard work will pay off.

To carry out a squat, all you have to do is:

1
Start with your feet shoulder-width apart.

2
Sit back as if you're sitting into an imaginary chair.

3
Ensure you keep your chest pushed out and heels on the floor throughout the movement.

4
Once your hips are as low as your knees, stand back up into your starting position.

5
You can use a pause at the bottom of the exercise, or even a jump at the end, to make it harder.

Exercise 4 – Lunges

The great thing about lunges is that they can be performed anywhere, at home or in the gym, and with or without weights. There are also many variations of lunges, including walking lunges, stationary lunges, and, reverse lunges, so if you feel the need to challenge yourself, you can always switch things up a bit. Lunges are perfect for hitting the quads, glutes, and hamstrings, and will also call your abs into play to help you maintain balance.

To carry out a lunge, all you have to do is:

1

Place hands on your hips, standing tall with your chest out.

2

Take a big step forward with one leg.

3

Lower your hips until your back knee is almost touching the floor.

4

Push through your front leg, and return to starting position.

5

Repeat on opposite leg.

Exercise 5 – Planks

In my eyes, planks are a great starting point for people who are new to exercise. They are so simple, but yet hugely beneficial. Just make sure you pay close attention to the directions so that your plank technique is 100% correct.

To carry out a plank, all you have to do is:

1

Starting with the pushup position is the easiest way to get into the plank.

2

Lower both your forearms to the ground so that both your elbows and fists are flat to the ground. Your palms should be balled up, and directly underneath your shoulders.

3

Curl your toes under and engage your abs by tilting your pelvis and pulling your belly button toward your spine.

4

Straighten your body but keep your neck and spine neutral. Imagine that you're a plank of wood, and that you're as straight as an arrow.

5

Flex your abdominals and squeeze your glutes. These are the two major muscle groups you'll be working out in this exercise.

6

Hold this position, also known as the plank, until after the burning begins. Keep your eyes on the floor in front of you. Avoid raising your behind. Your body should make a straight line from your heels to the back of your head.

The routine

What I suggest you do is use these five exercises as a circuit style workout. This means you will go from one exercise straight in to the next one until you have done all five. Once you have completed all five, take a one minute break to re-hydrate and concentrate on your breathing, before then repeating the lot. Aim to do this five times.

1. Burpees (x 10)
2. Squats (x 20)
3. Mountain climbers (x 20 each leg)
4. Lunges (x 20 each leg)
5. Plank (hold for 30 seconds)

Aim to carry out the programme of exercises at least 4–5 times a week, and before you know it, you will be surprising yourself with the results.

This routine is challenging, and you will definitely be out in a sweat by the end of it, but don't let that put you off from continuing with your programme. These exercises will burn plenty of calories while at the same time hitting as many muscles as possible.

Yes it will be tough, but the reality is that an easy fitness routine won't give you results. What you will find however, is that the more you carry out this programme, the more your body becomes accustomed to it, and as such, it won't knock as much breath out of you as it did in the beginning.

The most important thing to remember is that this is just a guide. Fitness levels can vary greatly from one individual to the next, so adjust the exercises to suit your own capabilities, and then work your way up. For instance, some people will be able to do less reps and time than others, while others will be able to do more, so just establish what you are capable of at first, and then aim to get a little bit better each day.

What's in Sue's Fridge?

I love my food but I try my best to eat well and stay healthy. After all, girls don't need to be stick thin as long as they're comfortable in their own bodies. I'm lucky to be naturally slim but even I have my body hang ups. I wish I had a more toned tummy. I hate my back fat where my bra sits. And yes... I have cellulite too. Nobody's perfect. Not you, not me, not that girl whose legs or lips or bum you'd kill for... even she will have some body part she's not totally happy with.

YOU SHOULDN'T STRIVE to look like someone else because no two people are meant to be the same. I've met so many readers at workshops, book signings and events over the past year and do you know what? You're all beautiful so keep doing what you're doing and if you pick up a tip or two from this section that's fantastic, but don't stress about it or head down to the local supermarket with a SoSueMe shopping list! Though lots of you asked me to talk about my daily diet in the book, please keep in mind that the foods I talk about below are what I aim to eat on a good day... but I'm human and I have my treat days and my visit to the take away at the end of a night out too.

Breakfast

I ALWAYS have this!

- ★ Flahavan's porridge with honey, cinnamon, and sometimes, whey powder too.
- ★ Fresh squeezed orange juice or a smoothie.
- ★ Barry's Tea

Snacks

- ★ Nuts and fruit
- ★ Smoothie, or protein shake

Lunch

- ★ A salad from the amazing 'Chopped' on Dublin's Baggot Street. I always choose the Asian Chicken Salad!
- ★ Chicken, basil, tomato, lettuce and onion wrap.
- ★ Fruit such as orange segments, an apple or some blueberries
- ★ Snack-a-Jack crisps
- ★ Glass of water

Dinner

- ★ Chicken stir fry
- ★ Chicken, vegetables, green beans, sweet potatoes with some potatoes.
- ★ Steak, mushrooms, vegetables and potatoes

The three rules I try to adhere to are:

1. Try not to eat carbs after 8pm
2. Drink at least 2 litres of water each day
3. Everything in moderation! If I want the Twix, I'll eat it! I just won't eat four a day!

I love bread, but bread definitely does not love me! It gives me really bad bloating and tummy pains, so when having lunch, I try to avoid it and choose a wrap instead.

From the Millie and Gym range at Life Style Sports. Runners by Nike.

What I Wore – Gym Edition

From the Millie and Gym range at Life Style Sports. Runners by Nike.

WHEN YOU ARE first starting out with an exercise programme, you can just wear anything that's comfortable and allows you to bend and stretch unrestricted. But if you find that you are enjoying going to the gym or even following a routine at home, it makes sense to invest in some good quality gym gear that keeps you cool and, when it comes to your footwear, offers you enough support.

Here are some of my gym favourites.

Adidas t-shirt
and leggings
with Nike
runners.

My Fitness Goals

Let's not do anything crazy here, like 0% body fat or running at the speed of sound! Setting yourself some small goals and recording how you get on means getting the feel goods each time you have a little achievement. It could be a 5k walk or simply detoxing for a week. It's up to you!

....
....
....
....
....
....
....
....
....
....
....
....
....
....
....
....
....
....
....
....
....

Chapter Six

Instagram

sosueme_ie

⏱ 2hr

First, Let Me Take a Selfie: SoSueMe's Guide to Instagram

 1086 likes

sosueme_ie Instagram & Selfies

●●●

The Saturday night outfit isn't complete until the obligatory selfie has been taken. Some will call us selfie-takers vain, but I don't care! If you're feeling good about yourself before you go out for the night, then why not take the selfie? I say go for it!

✼✼✼✼✼✼✼✼✼✼✼✼✼✼✼✼✼✼✼✼✼✼✼✼✼✼✼✼✼✼

How to Take the Perfect Instagram Picture

Lighting

The right lighting is crucial. Always try to use natural light, rather than using the built-in flash. Rarely will the flash produce flattering results because it's just way too harsh. If you're a serial selfie-taker and find that you often get frustrated with the lighting then grab yourself an app to alter the photo.

Filter

Seriously, what did we do before Instagram filters?! HELLO VALENCIA! Filters can make or break a selfie. The right filter can make an otherwise bland photo brilliant, and let's face it, when the lighting isn't quite perfect, there is nothing like a filter to save the shot! There's a happy medium to be found in filtering though. Don't over-filter, and don't use the same filter for each image. Play around with your options. Choosing the right filter will give you a brilliant result, but make the mistake of over-filtering the image and you will be left with barely distinguishable facial features. See which filter works best for you, and remember, if the dark eye circles from a late night out are still looking a bit too obvious for comfort, there are always the black and white filters! Filters are indeed wonderful for improving an image, but don't forget that sometimes a picture can look just as good, if not better, without one. This brings me to my next point...

Edit

If you don't want to use a filter but do want to slightly improve the picture, then you should check out the range of photo editing apps available. A few changes to the picture's saturation, temperature depth, contrast, and brightness levels can make a massive difference. Just make sure you don't over-edit otherwise it will look unnatural!

Background

There is nothing like an untidy room to destroy an otherwise perfect selfie. When someone views your selfie or any picture you put on Instagram for that matter, the first thing they should see is the subject you are photographing. Nothing should take the focus away from a selfie or a picture unless of course it's a funny photo bomb! (Remember Zach Braff photo-bombing a couple's wedding photograph in Times Square? Not a selfie, I know, but still, it was a hilarious photo bomb!) Overall however, if you want your images to be flattering, then everything about the image has to be flattering and this very much includes the background. Also, try to vary the locations of your selfies as much as possible. Keep it interesting. If every single selfie you take is in a bathroom or a bedroom, then people will get bored and you'll end up portraying yourself as someone who doesn't get out very much. Your selfie should reflect your personality, so make it fun!

Angle

Never look down at the camera. This will give you a double chin! Either hold the phone at face level or up high above your head, but never below your chin. Ever!

Your good side

We all have our good angles, and we all most certainly have our bad angles. To find out your most flattering side, do what the models do and practice in front of a mirror! Take lots of selfies with your head tilted a little, and eventually you will see which side suits you best! When taking multiple selfies in a bid to find the right one, don't constantly press the shoot button otherwise most of the pictures will come out blurred. Take your time.

Duck face

Pulling a Kardashian pout, or a duck face as it's also known, is absolutely fine. In fact, when it's done right, it can be quite nice. Try to limit the number of times you pull this expression though! There is nothing worse than when someone uploads an album of selfies and their only expression is of their lips puckered and their cheeks sucked in. Pouting is fine in a few images, but nothing beats a nice smile!

Remove the cover

Remove the phone cover. Yes I know there is a hole in the phone cover for the camera lens, but removing the cover can very often produce a better picture. Try it!

Straighten

Don't ignore the straightening tool. Straightening an image might seem like a tiny adjustment, but trust me, it's a noticeable one. Use it!

Caption

The caption gets just as much attention as the picture does, so don't leave it blank! The best captions are creative and entertaining.

How to Get More Followers and Likes

★ Study the accounts of mega successful Insta-figures. Fame brings with it an automatic social media following, but the accounts I'm talking about are the ones belonging to individuals who are not Hollywood famous, but whose follower figures would almost have you believe they are. Ask yourself, what is their Instagram personality? Are they witty, creative, fashionable? Identify what it is about their pictures that attracts so many followers?

★ Maximise your chances of acquiring new followers by posting at times of peak traffic. Refrain from posting in the middle of the night. It is estimated that an Instagram picture will remain in the news feed of your followers for around four hours, so if you post at 3am, your followers may never see it. To find out the best time to post, just click on 'statistics' on the home navigation menu and then hit on 'optimisation'. This will give you all the deets you need!

★ According to the massively successful visual analytics and marketing firm, Curalate, bright images on Instagram receive more likes than dark ones. Similarly, images that contained plenty of background were also more popular than ones where the image was tightly cropped. Pictures with 'texture' were also found to be a magnet for likes on Instagram. Interestingly, Curalate also found that images of low saturation received more 'likes' than photos with vibrant colours, so start using those filters!

★ Don't neglect your current followers when in pursuit of new ones. Interact with those following you and reply to any comments they leave. If they compliment you, take the time to thank them.

An example of strong Instagram activity

- People can't follow you if they don't see you, so get out there and start liking and commenting! You need to fully engage in the Instagram community. Comment on images, chat with other users, and always be on the lookout for new accounts to follow.

- Apparently, #love frequently tops the list as the most popular Instagram hashtag. Hashtags can help bring your posts to a wider audience so make sure to use the ones that are most relevant to the image and the kind of followers you want to attract. If you are posting a selfie, hashtag the names of the cosmetics you used, e.g. #nakedpalette #MAC.

- Connect your Instagram account with your Facebook account. After all, your Facebook friend list is a ready-made pool of potential followers so it makes sense to merge the two.

- Ask questions in the picture caption. This encourages interaction, which is essential when

it comes to acquiring new followers. For instance, before heading out on a night, post a picture of two outfits and ask your followers which one you should wear. Posts such as this will persuade people to comment as well as catch the eye of those interested in style and fashion.

- If you are using Instagram to promote your business, then it's important that you include your Instagram username wherever possible, like for example, on your business card, LinkedIn profile, Twitter bio, or beneath your signature in an email. You catch my drift.

- It might sound obvious, but if you want people to follow you, you have to give them a good reason. Be as creative as you can and look to other accounts for inspiration. Don't litter your Instagram with selfies or images of your cat, vary the style of photograph as much as you can. Make good use of the filters too, but avoid using the same one over and over again, otherwise it will extract the colour and eccentricity from your page. If you are not using a filter, make sure you hashtag #nofilter.

- Don't post a ton of photos at once! That might be fine for Facebook, but it won't work on Instagram. Instead, space out the images over a couple of days.

- For the best images, explore! Go somewhere you have never been before, and when you get there, photograph the hell out of it!

The Big Question

✿✿✿

Are you really that attractive or is your selfie game just strong?

That attractive

Go on, tick
this one!

Strong selfie game

Chapter Seven

Pals, Pooches and SoSueMe HQ:
SoSueMe Gets Personal

One boyfriend, two gorgeous Maltese dogs and about a billion Yankee Candles!

Welcome to my home!

SoSueMe HQ – The Beauty Room!

MY OFFICE IS the nerve centre of SoSueMe. It's where everything happens. When Dylan and I moved in together, one of the first things I set about doing was turning the spare room into an office. I am constantly blogging about fashion and beauty products so it made sense for me to have a home office. I am in that room all the time; I just love working in there! One half of the room is very business-like. It's where I keep my computer, my reams of business details, client folders, blogging ideas, Filofax, contracts, and everything else that goes with running a business. The other half of the room is where I have my make-up shelves, my nail varnish racks, my second wardrobe, as well as my mirror and lights for when I am recording my YouTube tutorials or just testing products. It's very SoSueMe!

I spend so much time in that one room. Honestly, you probably wouldn't believe just how many hours I am in my office each week. This is why it was important to me to create a space that I would enjoy working in. When I was first putting it together, I wanted it to be a very pretty, clean and simple, professional-looking blogging room, which, I'm proud to say, it now is! I pretty much do everything in there – I get ready there whenever I am heading out, I work and blog there constantly, and I also record some YouTube videos in there. It is also where I keep the beautiful mementos sent to me from fans. Many SoSueMe readers have sent me some of the most amazing letters and tokens, and I treasure every single one of them!

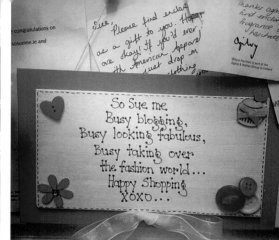

75

My Best Pals

MY FRIENDS MEAN the world to me. They're mad, fun, caring, and unpredictable, and I would be absolutely lost without them. I think every girl would choose to have 5 best friends rather than 100 fake friends, and I count myself very lucky to have found my perfect 5! Lots of you will recognise my friends from the photos on the SoSueMe.ie Facebook and Instagram accounts, so I thought I would share with you how each of us first met.

Sara Ward – The mother hen!

I randomly met Sara in the Wright Venue one night back in 2008. We had a friend in common, and when Sara and I got chatting, we just immediately became pals. She is without doubt my closest friend now. If I'm upset, or if I am ever having a bad day she is the girl I know I can turn to. She is the mother of our group and she is definitely the kind of best friend every girl should have. I stay at her place at least once a month, and she also stays at mine from time to time. I love hanging out with her, and likewise my little sister Erica loves hanging out with Sara's little daughter, Isabelle. Sara has a wonderful maternal nature about her and is an amazing mum to Isabelle.

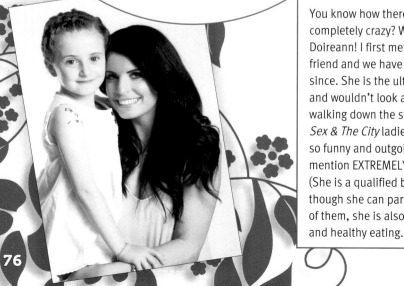

Doireann Gately – The cheeky, brainy one of the group!

You know how there is always one girl who is so much fun and just completely crazy? Well in our gang, that girl is Doireann! I first met Doireann through a friend and we have been great pals since. She is the ultimate glam girl and wouldn't look a bit out of place walking down the street with the *Sex & The City* ladies! She is so funny and outgoing, not to mention EXTREMELY intelligent. (She is a qualified barrister!) Even though she can party with the best of them, she is also mad into yoga and healthy eating.

Joanne Martin – The lady of the group!

I first met Joanne through modelling. We became friends straight away and have been the best of friends ever since. She is always such a bubbly girl, and without a doubt, the sweetest person I have ever met.

I don't think I have ever heard her say a bad word about anyone. She got married earlier this year too! Her wedding was one of the most amazing I have ever been to, and she looked so beautiful in her Vera Wang gown.

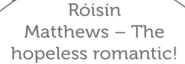

Róisín Matthews – The hopeless romantic!

There is always one girl in every group who everyone turns to for advice, and for our group, that girl is Róisín! I actually met Róisín through Sara, and she has since become one of my best friends. Roisin is the one I have Nandos dates and cinema dates with every week, and when we were both single, we would spend our dates mainly talking about boys! Róisín is very straight with people in that she will always listen to both sides of the story and give you a direct answer. She is also really funny and extremely caring.

Kim Kearns – The party animal

Kim is the sort of girl who is quiet until you get to know her. She and I are very alike in terms of personality and we have a very similar sense of humour too. Whenever we meet up, we spend most of the time laughing and having the best of craic! She is so much fun to hang out with and I always love heading out for drinks with her. In saying that, Kim would also have a serious side to her and she doesn't take any crap. She has her head firmly screwed on.

When I Met Dylan

YOU KNOW HOW they always say that the guy you are going to end up with is most likely right in front of you already? Well, for me, that was literally the case! I am great pals with a guy called Brook; I have known him for years, and his best friend was a guy called Dylan O'Connor. I often spotted Dylan out with Brook, but I had never really spoken to him because he was a very quiet person and pretty much kept to himself. So one night, we were all out together in Brook's nightclub, The Wright Venue, and at the time, I had been single for around two years, but Dylan had just come out of a relationship. At some point during the night, we both got chatting and just hit it off. It was funny, we had been in each other's general company so many times before, but we hadn't ever spoken properly until that night.

That was a little over two years ago, and we have been together ever since! Last November, we made the decision to move in together and now we are happier than ever in our own place with our dogs Coco and Harper. Dylan has been the most amazing support to me throughout this often crazy journey of mine. He has encouraged me through the bad days, helped me celebrate the good days, and reassured me during the stressful ones. He goes everywhere with me, and there really is nothing like having that kind of support when the nerves are kicking in before a big event! He is the most caring, outgoing guy, and so much fun to be around. Everyone who meets him immediately warms to him, because he has such a lovely nature. I was never the kind of girl who 'needed' a guy, but now that I have a truly genuine person by my side, I know I definitely wouldn't ever choose to be without him. Having someone like Dylan who really cares for me, well all I can say is that it's the best feeling in the world. I am still as much in love with him now as I was the day I met him!

79

My Family!

I AM HONESTLY blessed to have grown up in such a loving family, and I really believe that having had such a strong positive foundation in those early years has moulded me into the kind of adult I am today. I have always been very close to my parents, and I credit them with having instilled in me the importance of hard work and setting goals. My family have long been an incredible source of inspiration to me, and they have always supported me through any project I turned my hand to. They are so caring, so encouraging, and not to mention so much fun! I love them to bits and I genuinely don't know where I would be today without them.

With my Mam, my youngest sister Katie and my Dad.

With my sisters Katie and Carla

With my Mam

Myself, my brother Robert and my
Mam last Christmas Day.

With Robert and his
fiancée Hayley on
New Year's Eve

Jerry \ Photography

Jerry \ Photography

On My Worst Days I Must Remember....

❋❋❋

Bad days are as inevitable as tan stains on a white shirt, but that's why we have mates, siblings, better halves, big brothers, little sisters...

What do they mean to you? What do love about them? Here's where you make that feel good list of memories, enviable talents and traits you've always admired. Required reading for days when you need a pick-me-up!

....
....
....
....
....
....
....
....
....
....
....
....
....
....
....
....

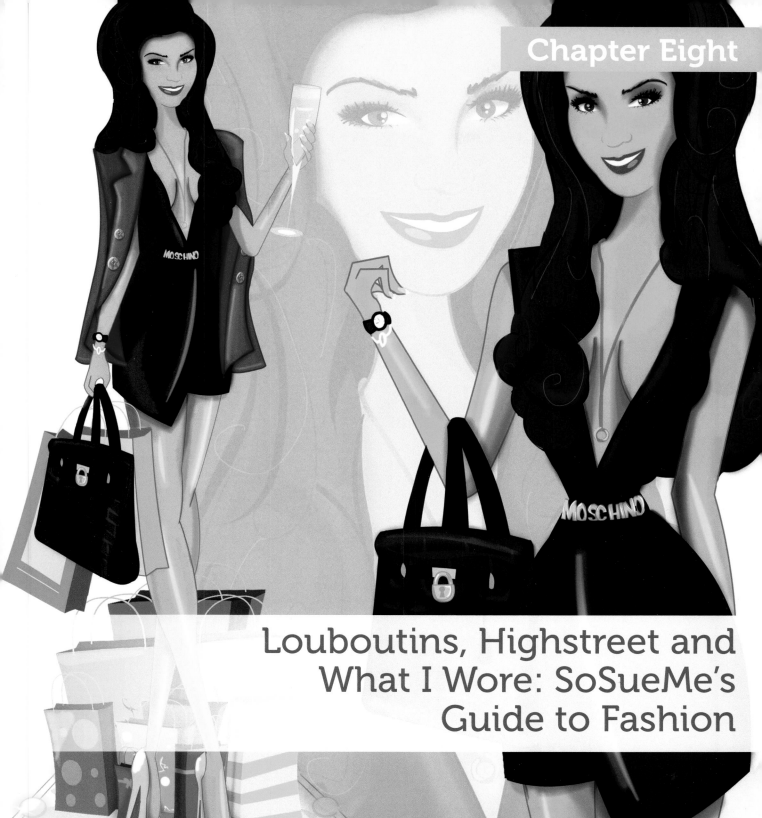

Chapter Eight

Louboutins, Highstreet and
What I Wore: SoSueMe's
Guide to Fashion

I LOVE FASHION; I love absolutely everything about it, so you can guess how excited I was when I got to attend New York Fashion Week this year. It was amazing to experience the shows and the clothes and to plan all my outfits for the trip... but more about that in the NYC chapter! What I really want to talk about here is how fashion can make you feel when you're ballsy enough to experiment with what you wear.

When something feels good on you, it can give you so much confidence. Every girl loves that feeling they get when they try on a fab dress and it looks as though it was made for them. When you wear something you love, whether it's a tailored pair of jeans and a stylish t-shirt, or an elegant Jovani dress and high heels, it just makes your smile that bit brighter and helps you feel really good about yourself.

I love it when readers get some style inspo from what I wear. Whenever I post a look on SoSueMe.ie, I always hope it will give ladies an idea of what pieces will work well together or what looks might suit them.

Most of all, though, I love the thrill of finding the perfect piece. I love splashing out on a favourite label to reward myself when I've put hours and months of work into a project. And I adore spending time mixing and matching my wardrobe to come up with new looks that make me feel good.

In my last book, I dedicated some space to What I Wore and recapped some of the outfits I'd previously posted online from events and nights out. It got a huge response from readers and this wouldn't be a SoSueMe.ie book if I didn't talk about the looks you loved, so there are plenty of them featured this time too including a section on my favourite outfits and a sneaky peek inside my handbag! You'll see that some of the pieces featured are things I picked up online, so I've included a guide to my fave online shopping haunts. As well as having a good nosey at the pieces I'm wearing, though, think about the different ways you could style them for yourself and have the confidence to wear what makes you feel good. That's what it's all about.

Looks You Loved

THE 'WHAT I WORE' section of SoSueMe.ie has always been one of the most popular with readers. It came about as a result of the number of questions I was getting about my outfits. I don't think I could even hazard a guess as to how many times I have heard the question, "Sue where do you get your dress/top/shoes?", so it made sense to set up a regular feature documenting what I was wearing and where each item could be found. Here are some of the looks you loved most from throughout the past twelve months!

Dress: Forever Unique: Cari's Closet
Shoes: Louboutin Lady Peeps

Dress: Zara
Hat: Suzanne Ryan Millinery
Shoes: Christian Louboutin

Judging the best dressed competition at the Limerick Races

Dress: Tempest Hunter midi dress

Dress: Starla Dress Rental
Bag: Chanel
Shoes: Christian Louboutin
Watch: Daniel Wellington

Channelling my inner Nicole Scherzinger for a nightclub appearance in Galway!

Skirt: River Island

Shirt: Zara

Shoes: Christian Louboutin

Necklace: Penneys

Dress: Starla Dress Rental

Bag: Mulberry

Shoes: Christian Louboutin

Jeans: Zara

Top: Zara

Shoes: Penneys

Scarf: Gucci

Clutch: Mulberry

About to see Beyoncé Live at The O2!

Jeans: Zara

Jacket: Vintagehorders.net

Hat: H&M

Top: Penneys

Boots: Louboutins

Denim Shorts: One Teaspoon from Bowtique

Shirt: Topshop

Shoes: River Island

Bag: Bowtique

Leather Jacket: Bowtique

Dress: Nicole Sherzinger Collection from Missguided

Bag: Chanel

Marbs!

When I holidayed in Marbella earlier this year, I posted some photographs of my outfits, some of which were from River Island. I later found out from River Island that they'd had 80,000 hits on their website as a result!

Dress: House of CB London

Shoes: Louboutins Lady Peeps

Earrings: Newbridge Silverware

Inside My Handbag

AS MUCH AS I love my shoes, I'm a total handbag girl at heart. I'm always on the go for work, which means I carry everything around with me so the kind of handbags I go for are BIG! Basically, if it wouldn't give the girl at the Aer Lingus check-in desk nightmares, it hasn't got enough space for my liking! I like to be prepared for every eventuality, and, in my line of work, anything can happen!

After I displayed the contents of my makeup bag in my first book, I got so many requests from readers wanting to take a peek inside my handbag too. So here it is!

Filofax

Prada sunglasses

iPad

Pen

Backcombing brush

Jo Malone fragrance

Makeup bag

SoSueMe.ie business cards

Mini toothbrush and toothpaste kit

Vaseline

Hairbrush

Michael Kors wallet

Sanitary hand wipes

iPhone and charger

Around 15,000 lip balms

Tissues

Denim Shorts – Worn x 4 Ways

SHORTS ARE ONE of those items that you can either dress up or dress down with a few clever accessories and yet still stay looking supremely stylish. There's just something about them that will be forever fashionable! Here, I show you four ways to wear the classic denims!

Online Shopping

I LOVE HITTING the shops – show me a girl who doesn't? And from the day smartphones were invented, I embraced online shopping quicker than you can say 'Add to Cart'! I love finding a bargain online or discovering a new fashionable corner of the internet where I haven't shopped before. Here are some of my faves.

The sites

Depop (App)

Chances are you have already seen one of your Facebook friends selling clothes on Depop. I'm on Depop and I love it! It's such a great way to get rid of items you haven't worn in years. This brilliantly stylish app allows you to buy and sell items straight from your phone. It's kind of like the Instagram equivalent of a trendy market! If you spot something you like, you can chat to the seller to ask questions and even haggle on the price. If the seller agrees to sell to you, they will make the 'buy' option visible and you simply pay via Paypal. Anyone can sell on Depop; all you have to do is take a picture of the outfit and post the size and price! What I really like about this website is that you can follow the accounts of your favourite sellers thus ensuring you never miss new additions.

Nastygal.com

This is a fab site and world famous for a good reason! If you haven't already checked it out, do so immediately! Nasty Gal has an amazing vintage section, however they also sell a huge range of other labels as well as their own designs. From quirky to elegant, there is something on this site for every taste. It's also very reasonably priced too so you get seriously fab style without the big credit card bill at the end of the month!

9crowstreet.com

9crowstreet.com is the online home of Irish vintage shop 9 Crow Street which is based on Dublin's north quays. If you live outside Dublin, or you just prefer shopping from the comfort of your couch, this website is the destination for vintage gear! Even in those weeks when you can't afford to shop for a much as a pair of Penneys plimsolls, this website is so beautifully put together (check out the Lookbooks!) that you can ALMOST satisfy your fashion cravings with a couple of hours ogling their latest finds.

The tricks

Shop in sterling

It doesn't apply to every site, but for some you'll find that simply changing the currency from Euro to UK sterling can save you an absolute chunk of change when it comes to rooting out the debit card and paying the total. It's particularly effective on Asos where you can usually save yourself the price of another skirt or blazer. If you're like me, you'll probably just use that money to buy another skirt or blazer, but hey, you tried, right?!

ParcelMotel

Is there anything more devastating than finding a piece you love, scrimping together the cash to buy it and typing in all your details only to be faced with the news that they don't deliver to Ireland? Nightmare. Or it was, before these guys came along. Set up an account and get your online shopping delivered to their Belfast depot (which counts as a UK address!) and then they forward it on to your nearest ParcelMotel. Takes the hassle out of trekking miles to the An Post office for your stuff as well when they can't fit the six handbags you splurged on through the letterbox. I love anything that takes the hassle out of shopping... as if I need an excuse!

SoSueMe Secret

Brides-to-be listen up! If you are shopping for a gown, have a look at the LDK range in Cari's Closet Bridal Boutique. LDK stands for Lisa Duffy Kavanagh, the owner of the fab Cari's Closet where I get a lot of my dresses from, and just a few months ago, she opened up a bridal boutique which features her own range of gowns. I swear I have never seen gowns as beautiful as those on the rails in her boutique. Lisa has such a great selection to suit all tastes and the brands she stocks are so beautifully elegant. They are just so different to what you normally see in bridal boutiques. Whenever I get engaged, Cari's Closet Bridal Boutique will be my first port of call!

My Favourite Shoes

Christian Louboutin Booties

I had been lusting after these booties for three years! I only decided to treat myself to them last Christmas after my publisher, John O'Connor, told me my book had made it into the bestsellers list again! It had spent 6 weeks in the list, so I marched straight into Brown Thomas and brought my beloved booties home once and for all! I was so delighted with how well the book had done that I wanted to mark the occasion in some way. I didn't want a tattoo, I didn't want a piercing, but I *did* want the booties, so I got them and wore them proudly all Christmas. My favourite memory is wearing them on Christmas Day when my Twitter was hopping with tweets from people who had woken up to find my book under the Christmas tree! I had put so much work into my first book, and it was such a lovely feeling knowing that the readers were enjoying it so much.

Christian Louboutin Pigalle Stilettos

I don't think I will ever forget the excitement of receiving these! My Pigalle stilettos were the first pair of Louboutins I ever received. It was a fab birthday present from my boyfriend Dylan and I can't tell you how much I love them. They're just so elegant. A total classic.

Christian Louboutin Lady Peeps

These were the first pair of Louboutins I ever bought for myself. I absolutely treasure them! I had received a call from *The Sunday World* telling me I had topped the public poll of Ireland's Sexiest Woman, and I also had my book launch taking place the following night, so I decided to celebrate with a pair of Louboutins. They were not my first pair, as Dylan had given me a gorgeous pair of Pigalles for my birthday, but they were the first pair I had bought for myself. I was proud that I could go in and buy them for myself. I work extremely hard to earn my money, so in my eyes, they are a symbol of accomplishment.

Pink River Island T-Bars

I first wore these T-Bar beauties to my best friend Joanne's hen party in Marbella. The plan was that the hens would wear black and Jo would wear white, so to add a splash of colour to my black dress, I decided to wear the pink t-bars. River Island later told me they had completely sold out of those shoes after I posted the pictures on SoSueMe.ie! I couldn't believe it!

Valentino inspired shoes from Savida

I was out shopping with my mum when I spotted these in Dunnes Stores. Straight away they reminded me of the Valentino shoes. Funnily enough, I had planned on buying a pair of Valentino shoes, but as soon as I saw those, I just thought wow. I actually liked them much better! They too sold out everywhere after I blogged about them.

"You can do anything you put your mind to, and you can do it in stilettos"
Kimora Lee Simmons

"If you haven't got it, fake it! Too short? Wear big high heels, but do practice walking!"
Victoria Beckham

"I am insecure. Everyone's insecure." Manolo Blahnik

My Top 10
Favourite Outfits

DESPITE HAVING WORN literally hundreds of glam outfits over the past year, there are still a few firm favourites that come to mind whenever readers ask me about the looks I loved most! So here, for the first time, I have decided to list my overall top ten favourite looks from 2014.

This fab little black party dress is from LillyCoo.com! The owner told me afterwards that it completely sold out within minutes of me posting it on my Facebook page. SoSueMe.ie readers have great taste in dresses!

Dress: Rachel Gilbert from Starla Dress Rental

Bag: Chanel

Shoes: Penneys

Dress: Starla Dress Rental

Bag: Mulberry

Shoes: Christian Louboutin

Top: H&M

Skirt: Zara

Brooch: Chanel

Shoes: River Island

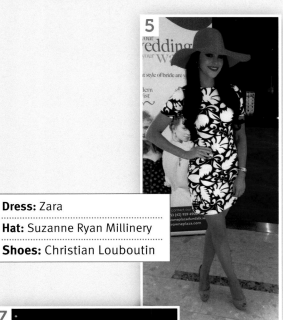

5

Dress: Zara
Hat: Suzanne Ryan Millinery
Shoes: Christian Louboutin

6

Oversized Coat: River Island
Mollie Jeans: River Island
White Crop T: H&M
Shoes: River Island
Clutch: Promod (Liffey Valley)
Belt: Hermes

8

Dress: Starla Dress Rental

7

I wore this dress to Joanne's wedding!
Dress: River Island

Jeans: Koral Los Angeles
Top: Oasis – Mollie King Collection
Necklace: Newbridge Silverware
Shoes: Christian Louboutin

9

10

Jeans: Penneys
T-Shirt: Zara
Blazer: Ollie & Mac Boutique
Bag: Michael Kors
Belt: Hermés
Boots: Christian Louboutins
Watch: Daniel Wellington
Earrings: 1920's Vintage
Bangles: Alex & Ani
Chain: MyNameNecklace

My Shopping List

Whether it's key pieces that'll last a lifetime or this season's highstreet must-haves, I hope this chapter has given you some wardrobe inspiration. It's time to make a shopping list!

....
....
....
....
....
....
....
....
....
....
....
....
....
....
....
....
....
....
....
....
....
....
....

Chapter Nine

SoSueMe GLAM:
SoSueMe's Guide to Beauty

EVER SINCE I was a little girl, I have loved make-up, and I count myself very lucky to be in a job where cosmetics play a huge role. I often get to test products before they have hit the shops, which is a dream for me, and I love being able to tell readers which ones are really worth their money. Whenever I find a great product, all I want to do is tell everyone how good it is!

It's amazing how finding a highlighter or eye shadow that you love can make you feel great – but when something works it works! Like everyone, though, I'm guilty of finding my favourites and wearing them all the time. In this chapter, even though I mention my faves, I would love if they inspire and encourage you guys to break out from the usual make-up routine and try something new!

My Latest Beauty Favourites!

Chanel Vitalumière Foundation

I love mixing some Chanel Vitalumière Foundation (shade 40 beige) with my Make Up Forever HD Foundation (shade m123). The result I get is just a dream!

Anastasia Beverly Hills Dipbrow Pomade

Ladies, I have tried all the different brow products, and I have yet to find one that beats the Dipbrow Pomade from Anastasia Beverly Hills. It is by far the best. Once you apply the product, it lasts for ages. I bought it from Sephora when I was in New York for fashion week, but it is also available from their website.

I also bought the Anastasia Beverly Hills Concealer Pencil for cleaning up around the brows after filling them in, and it's just so good. I actually find myself wondering how on earth I managed before I got them!

MeMeMe Angel Arch Brow Gel

To help keep my brows firmly in place, I slick on some MeMeMe Angel Arch Brow Gel. This little gem is amazing! It holds the shape of your brows and prevents any stray hairs from moving out of place!

Magnetic Lash – Lash Extension Mascara

This revolutionary cosmetic has even found its way into the pages of *Vogue*!

If you have used it, you will know what the fuss is all about. It literally thickens your lashes. Yes, literally! With Magnetic Lash, you are basically attaching lots of tiny fibres to your lashes, but don't worry, the process itself is far more straightforward than it sounds! You first apply a coat of the mascara, followed by a coat of the fibres, before finishing with one last coat of mascara to seal the fibres in place. In the space of a minute, you have longer, thicker lashes! When it comes to mascaras in general, I also really like the Lancôme range. They will never let you down.

No.7 Instant Radiance Balm Highlighter

I am addicted to highlighters! I am constantly in search of the product that will give me the ultimate result of gorgeously dewy skin! My current favourite is No. 7's Instant Radiance Balm. I apply this balm prior to my foundation and it never fails to light up my face. I love it!

I love the glow I get from No.7's Instant Radiance balm

Inglot Sparkling Dust

Another highlighting product I cannot live without is the sparkling dust from Inglot. In fact, if I'm travelling somewhere and I forget to bring this with me, I genuinely get upset! THAT'S how much I love it! I always use it on the inner corners of my eyes and on the tips of my cheekbones.

Laura Mercier Primer

I was never really into primers... UNTIL I was introduced to the Laura Mercier foundation primer. Now I don't know how I got by without one before! I use it religiously. I used it for the photo shoot for this book and even after a long day, my make-up hadn't even budged! I especially love the Laura Mercier radiance primer as it gives my make-up a fab glow.

Rimmel's Glam Eyes Liquid Liner

If you are not particularly good at applying eye liner then you will love Glam Eyes Liquid Liner from Rimmel. Application is a doddle, and if you make a mistake, it's very easy to correct it without making a total mess of your eye make-up.

Inglot Gel Liner

When it comes to gel liners, Inglot gel liner is my favourite.

That said, if you find it hard to work with because of how fast it sets, then just get yourself the Inglot Duraline. This baby is a transforming liquid that will turn the Inglot powders and gels into a liquid form, making them easier to apply.

Urban Decay Primer Potions

When it comes to eye shadow primers, you can't go wrong with Urban Decay Primer Potions. Uh-maz-ing!

Fuschia Mineral Foundation

Not technically a setting powder, I know, but I use it as one!

I was never that into mineral foundations because I found them to be quite drying, but then I tested Fuschia's Mineral Foundation and I was duly converted! This particular mineral foundation has no talc in it, so no dryness thank God! When I use it on its own, I get a lovely dewy glow and fantastic coverage! More often than not however, I will use it as a setting powder over my own foundation just to keep it nicely in place. A dusting of Fuschia Mineral powder over my foundation is all it takes to keep it from budging or smudging! If you have oily skin, this foundation is definitely worth a try. It's also a wonderful starter foundation for girls who might be a little young for the heavy make-up look, or who might want good coverage without it being too noticeable at school!

Nude 'tude palette by theBalm

When I first used this eye shadow palette, I loved it so much, I ended up using it for weeks on end. The shades are so beautiful. I'm telling you, just try it for yourself and you will see exactly what I am talking about! One of the best, definitely!

Mary-Lou Manizer Highlighter

This is undoubtedly one of the best highlighting powders I have ever used. A light dusting of this will give the skin such a gorgeous glow with a nice hint of a gold shimmer. It looks especially beautiful when dusted onto tanned skin. I always dust some onto my face, collarbone, shoulders, and décolletage.

NYX Lipsticks

I am loving loving LOVING the range of NYX lipsticks and butter glosses.

I recently wore the pink one (shade 02) which SoSueMe.ie readers went crazy for!

Their range of butter glosses, which are all suitably named after gorgeous desserts, are also just to die for.

My favourites are:

★ Peach Cobbler
★ Cherry Pie (for over my lipstick)
★ Strawberry Parfait
★ Merengue
★ Vanilla Cream Pie (Such a gorgeous pinky nude)
★ Fortune Cookie (A nude shade that is particularly fab for day wear)

Peach cobbler

Strawberry parfait. My fave!

Vanilla cream pie

Fortune cookie

Rimmel Wake Me Up Concealer

I love using Rimmel's Wake Me Up Concealer whenever I want to brighten the area underneath my eyes. It gives tired eyes a real boost! It also has brilliant coverage.

Crown Brush Smoke It Out Eye shadow Palette

I love dramatic eyes, and this palette never fails to help me create the perfect dramatic eye! It consists of 36 shades in both matte and shimmer. It also includes warm and cold colours in light shades for highlighting and dark shades for shadowing. You have no idea how often I use this beauty of a palette. For make-up lovers, it's a dream to work with!

SoSueMe Secret

Don't ever be afraid to mix your foundations. Kim Kardashian does this all the time, and whether you love her or hate her, you can't deny, her make-up never looks less than immaculate! In this photograph, I am wearing a mixture of Glo Minerals Luxe Foundation (Burlee tone) and Crown Brush Illuminating Liquid foundation (FK115 22)

Lipsticks You Will Love

I AM ALWAYS asked about my lipsticks. In fact, whenever I post a style picture on Instagram or Facebook, I just know I will receive as many questions about my lipstick as I will about the outfit itself. I think every make-up loving girl is always on the lookout for the perfect lip colour. After all, it can totally enhance or transform your look. I don't know about you guys, but I always feel as though I am never fully ready until I have my lipstick and lip-gloss on.

As I get asked so many questions about lip colours and the different ones I wear, I decided to compile a collection of my own personal favourites!

Fuchsia – Party Girl

Inglot 601

No7 – Love Red

Fuchsia – VAMP

Bourjois Rouge Edition Orange Pop Up

MAC's Girl About Town.

NYX Butter Gloss – Strawberry Parfait

Rimmel By Kate Moss – Lipstick Code 101 / Kardashian Beauty Gloss, 'In The Flesh'

Kate Moss by Rimmel – Lipstick Code 03 / Max Factor Gloss – Nude

No7 BB Lips Beauty Balm – Orange Tube

Inglot Soft Peach Lip Paint.

Fuschia Lip Liner / No 7 Love Red Lipstick

103

My Crown Brush Favourites!

EVEN THOUGH I am the Irish ambassador for Crown Brush UK, I will only ever talk about the products that I love and can 100% recommend! There is no way I would put my name to something that isn't up to the SoSueMe.ie standard, simply because I would have too much to lose in terms of integrity. So many readers place great faith and trust in my reviews and there is just no way I would mislead them. As I mentioned earlier in the book, I had been a huge fan of Crown Brush long before my ambassador role came about and had used their brushes ever since a makeup artist friend recommended them to me. When I later used their concealer palette as part of a contouring demo on YouTube, the video was a massive hit. The success of the video subsequently led to Crown Brush asking me to be their Irish spokesperson, and I can honestly say, it has been an absolute dream working with a brand I love. In the past year alone, they have expanded their range to include blusher and eye shadow palettes as well as foundations and bronzers. I am always asked about my favourite Crown Brush products, so here are my top 5!

141 likes

crownbrushuk Hard at work in the Crownbrush office! It's been lovely having @sosueme_ie here with us! ♥

marthamccarthy Love the blazer

1. Illuminating Foundation

I loved the thick consistency of this foundation. It gives my skin that lovely hydrated feeling and it blends in perfectly too. The bottle states that the coverage is light-to-medium but I would definitely say the coverage is more of a medium-to-full, which suits me as I love foundations that offer a natural looking dewy finish, but yet can still hide your blemishes. At times I did notice that the pump action wasn't work as well as usual, but Crown Brush informed me that this is due to a lack of air getting in. If this happens to you, all you have to do is unscrew the top to allow some air in and then it should be back working perfectly again. I am currently using shade FK115 which is ideal for my skin tone, especially when I am wearing a tan. If I want to tone it down, then I either mix it with Crown Brush foundation number FK101, or my Makeup Forever HD Foundation, shade 123. These foundations are perfect for normal, oily and dehydrated skin types, however, here's a tip to bear in mind: anyone with an oily skin type should first powder their T-zone when using this foundation because it does produce a fab dewy finish. I understand that it's a bit risky purchasing a foundation online without having tested it first, so if you are unsure of what shade would suit your skin tone, then I would recommend that you get in touch with Crown Brush via their live chat.

I love to use the shade FK115 because it blends so perfectly into my skin, especially if I am wearing a tan

2. Rose Gold Highlighting Serum

I have fallen in love with this rich rose gold highlighting serum. It just instantly makes your skin look so much better. You can wear it with a foundation or on its own with a tan, the result is a gorgeous radiant bronzed effect. You can also use it on your neck, collarbone, shoulders, anywhere you want a beautiful bronzed shimmer! It's just amazing for a glam night time look and it gives the skin such a beautiful glow.

3. Corrector Palette

I LOVE this palette! As you know, highlighting and contouring is my forte, and this new palette is wonderful for creating a sleek contoured look. I used the shade next to the lilac tone for my highlighter, and the extra dark colour for my contour. The key to highlighting and contouring is to blend, blend and then blend even more. It takes time, but the final look is so worth it. The concealers all offer full opaque coverage and are extremely easy to apply. When I blogged about this palette after it first came out, some readers asked about the light green and lilac concealers. These are corrective concealers. The lilac colour is great for brightening the eye area and for covering/hiding dark circles, while the light green concealer will counteract any redness, which is perfect for anyone who suffers with high cheek pigmentation, rosacea, etc.

4. Blusher Palette

This palette contains 10 matte and shimmer shades that can be used for blush, contouring, or bronzing. The peachy shades are perfect for adding depth to the cheeks and giving a polished finish to any make-up look, while the shimmer shades really highlight your skin and add that splash of colour. The thing about blusher is you need to find a balance between too little and too much, so as always, application is everything! My rule of thumb is to only apply blusher to the apples of the cheeks. I always start applying my blush about two finger widths away from my nose, this helps to create a fresh, natural, and more of an effortless look. Another important point to remember is, instead of swirling the brush on your cheeks as you apply the colour, you will get a better result if you just lightly pat the blusher brush onto the skin.

5. Brush Shampoo

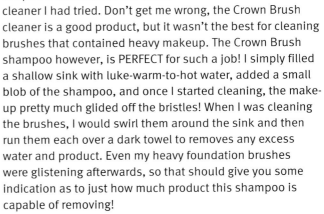

I was very impressed with the results of this brush shampoo, and found it to be far superior to the previous Crown Brush brush cleaner I had tried. Don't get me wrong, the Crown Brush cleaner is a good product, but it wasn't the best for cleaning brushes that contained heavy makeup. The Crown Brush shampoo however, is PERFECT for such a job! I simply filled a shallow sink with luke-warm-to-hot water, added a small blob of the shampoo, and once I started cleaning, the make-up pretty much glided off the bristles! When I was cleaning the brushes, I would swirl them around the sink and then run them each over a dark towel to removes any excess water and product. Even my heavy foundation brushes were glistening afterwards, so that should give you some indication as to just how much product this shampoo is capable of removing!

My Latest Skincare Favourites

WHEN IT COMES to skincare, I love nothing more than finding a new gem. Even though my list of favourite products changes each year, I do have a few staples that I am incredibly loyal to, primarily because no other products rival the results they produce. I know what I like, and, more importantly, I know what works for my skin type. I cannot stress enough how crucial it is to develop a good skincare routine. It's never too late to make a difference to the appearance of your skin, and the right products can do just that. The right lifestyle is also equally as important. You can't expect your skin to look perfect if you are treating your body in a way that is anything but. Smoking, junk food, lack of fresh air and lack of exercise are just some of the enemies of good skin. UV rays are another. Don't over-expose yourself to sun. Yes we all look good with a tan, but that's why we have fake tan, which I will be discussing later in this chapter. Regardless of the weather outside, you should use an SPF every day. Even an overcast day can leave you with sun damage and sun spots in years to come. When it comes to skincare, the choices you make today really do determine how you will look tomorrow!

People are always asking me about my skincare routine and what products I would recommend, so now I am about to tell you all about my latest favourites! These are definitely my top picks out of all the products I have tested this year.

Thalgo Pure Freshness Tonic Lotion / Elemis Apricot Toner

Declaré Gentle Cleansing Milk

As I have dehydrated skin, I am always careful not to use a cleanser that might dry it out even more. Instead, I use a milk or a lotion, and at the moment, I am loving the Declaré Gentle Cleansing Milk. It's so hydrating. It's also designed for sensitive skin, and at times, my skin can indeed be quite sensitive, especially around my cheeks.

There are only two types of toners that I use, and one of them is Thalgo Pure Freshness Tonic Lotion. It's such a good product and it wonderfully improves the appearance of your skin. I raved about this product in last year's book too, and I can tell you now, it is still most definitely a favourite. I don't like using toners that contain alcohol, because alcohol just strips the skin of its natural oils, dries it out even more and causes breakouts. It's fine to use if you have oily skin, but not otherwise. With some toners, you can even smell the alcohol in them, but that's not the case with this Thalgo gem! Another alcohol-free toner that I love is the Elemis Apricot Toner. I even have a travel-sized bottle of it to bring with me whenever I am travelling.

Kinvara Skincare Rosehip Face Serum

If I had to use just one skincare product for the rest of my life, this is the one I would undoubtedly choose. It's like an intense care treatment for your skin, and oh my God, talk about a difference in my skin when I use it! My skin feels so fresh and dewy, and my make-up goes on so much better. I bring it with me everywhere because I do tend to work late, fly a lot, and often have to wear heavy make-up for events, so this serum gives my skin the care it needs. It's like a rescue remedy. It's 100% organic and it smells amazing. It's my must-have product.

Thalgo Crème Silicium Regard

As I am turning 30 this year, I have to start looking after the delicate skin around my eyes. Since 25 onwards, I have noticed a few lines starting to form around my eyes and to keep these at bay for as long as possible, I invest in a wonderful eye cream and I use it religiously. The chemist ranges are fantastic, but really and truly, when you are dealing with the delicate eye area, you should get yourself a top quality dermatology cream. Elemis, Darphin, Thalgo, and Clarins are the brands I would recommend.

Darphin Hydraskin Rich Moisturiser / Elemis Collagen Cream

After I have applied my serum, I always slick on some moisturiser. This locks the serum into the skin.
At the moment, I am using the Darphin Hydraskin Rich Moisturiser. Not a lot of people would be familiar with this brand because it's not very easy to get. I only first came across it after I went to Carton House Spa for a facial and the girls there told me about it. It works brilliantly and is undoubtedly one of my two favourite moisturisers. Elemis Collagen Cream is my other fave! It's fantastic!

Elemis SOS Emergency Cream

The best problematic cream I turn to on those days when I get a time-of-the-month break out is Elemis SOS Emergency Cream. I have to take my hat off to Elemis; they have some seriously wonderful products. Their SOS cream really stood to me when I broke out in red rash recently. So many make-up artists had been doing my make-up at the time for different events, and I think one of them had been cleaning her brushes with spirits because I could even get the smell of the spirits from the brushes at the time. Not long afterwards, I developed a small red rash-like patch of skin on my face, which I couldn't get rid of! I went to Elemis for a facial, and when I explained my problem, they recommended the SOS cream. Not long after using it, the patch completely disappeared. The SOS cream is not something I use everyday, but it becomes part of my skincare regime whenever I need to get rid of a breakout, etc. This SOS cream is also a popular cream amongst people suffering from psoriasis and eczema.

No 7 Instant Radiance Beauty Balm

The No 7 Instant Radiance Beauty Balm is the product I turn to whenever my skin needs a pick-me-up. I smooth it on after my moisturiser and because it's a radiance balm, it has this gorgeous pinky pearly iridescent tone, which makes your skin glow. I use it everyday, but it's especially fantastic for when you are tired because it makes your face look so fresh. It's also a really good product to use prior to your make-up because of the dewy sheen it gives the skin.

Thalgo Oxygen 3 Defense Fluid SPF 5

I am a huge fan of SPF. I particularly like the Thalgo brand of sunscreen because it has quite a thin consistency and doesn't smell like an SPF. The Thalgo name is one of the most reputable when it comes to the skincare industry, and SPF is definitely a product you don't want to skimp on in terms of quality.

GlamGlow Youth Mud

If my skin looks dull or if I notice my make-up going patchy then I know its time for an intensive face mask. I love using the GlamGlow Youth Mud. This is a tingling exfoliating face mask that dries hard on your face. For a softer, brighter complexion, I try to apply the Youth Mud once a week, however if I want to re-hydrate my skin, I will use GlamGlow's new face mask, Thirsty Mud. This hydrating treatment is one I like to use after I have been travelling. I should point out that because the GlamGlow mud draws out all the impurities from the skin, some people might find that

GlamGlow Thirsty Mud

it will cause their skin to break out a little. It really all depends on your skin type so make sure you read up on it first before you buy.

SoSueMe Secret

Whenever I go to Galway, I always try to pop into Anna Forde and her team in The Beauty Suite in Tuam. I have been raving about the Beauty Suite ever since I had the most amazing facial there! The treatment was called the CACI Facial, and I can totally understand now why it's seen as the A-List secret to younger looking skin. It's a non-surgical facelift and it is also a wonderful alternative to Botox! So if you want younger looking skin without the use of needles, the CACI Facial is the one to try.

Grainne, Myself, Anna & Ewa

The Beauty Suite - Tuam

June 2013

It plumps and lifts the skin and leaves it feeling SO soft. I couldn't get over how smooth and soft my skin felt afterwards. The results lasted ages too. Now I know why JLo bought her very own CACI machine, not to mention, why her skin is always glowing! The process was very simple. Anna first buffed my skin and carried out a light microdermabrasion. Now, I've had bad experiences with microdermabrasions in the past, but Anna put it on the lowest setting possible, and it felt absolutely fine. It totally lifted the dead skin cells. The mask itself was AMAZING! — It is intensively moisturising and really transforms the skin. Anna also used a roller-like motion to massage in the moisture which felt so incredibly relaxing!

Once the treatment was finished, I could see a noticeable difference in my skin. It had such a healthy glow and those fine lines were much less obvious. My makeup just glided on so smoothly that evening, and when I posted some pictures of Dylan and I out at dinner later that night, a number of readers even commented on my dewy-looking skin! I'm telling you guys, that facial is amazing! Anna has such a wide range of treatments so you will definitely find one to suit your skin type. You can check out all her treatments on **www.thebeautysuite.com**.

With the ultra-glam Anna Forde of
The Beauty Suite in Tuam

My skin was glowing
after the facial

So Tan Me
My Tanning Dos & Don'ts

DO YOU REMEMBER Casper The Friendly Ghost? Well, without a tan, I am as white as he is, if not whiter in fact!

My pale Irish genes have fated me to a life of spray tans and tanning mitts, but I'll happily put up with it because I love the confidence a nice tan gives me! I am always asked about my tanning regime, especially when I post holiday snaps. I spoke about tanning in one of my YouTube videos, but I decided to keep the full list of tanning secrets for my book!

DON'T

Don't vigorously rub the tanning lotion into the skin. When you rub it in, you create friction and heat, both of which are big no-no's when it comes to achieving the perfect colour! Instead, pat the tan onto the skin and gently blend it in. It will make a huge difference.

DON'T

Don't apply your tan straight after a shower without first misting your skin with water! In order for a tan to develop right, your skin's pH level needs to be balanced, which, following a shower, it is anything but! This is why some tans develop into a shade of orange rather than bronze! To lower your pH level, just mist your skin with water and let the moisture be absorbed. Once completely dry, you can apply your tan!

DON'T

Don't ever leave the top off your tan bottle! When air gets in, it does some nasty stuff to your tan's ingredients. In short, it can turn your tan a slight shade of green! Not even on Paddy's Day would you get away with that look!

DON'T

Don't assume that the more fake tan you apply in one sitting, the darker it will develop! Most of it will come off in the shower! Your skin can only take so much, so anything more than, say, two coats, is just a waste. If you want a darker tan, wait until the following day and then apply another layer.

DO

Do rub the tiniest amount of moisturiser into areas such as your elbows, wrists, backs of the knees, eyebrows, and anywhere your tan is likely to gather. The cream will act as a barrier and prevent the tan from gathering in those troublesome places! Don't worry you wont be left with white patches in these places. The colour will still develop, it just won't gather.

DO

Do be careful with the kind of products you use on your fake tan once it has developed. Body oils, and moisturisers containing oils, can often weaken the fake tan, thus causing it to fade faster.

DO

Do take your time. You will be less likely to make mistakes if you don't rush! Take a half hour to yourself and do it right!

DO

Don't even think of skipping the exfoliating part! Exfoliation leaves your skin smooth and even, which means any tanning product you apply stands a greater chance of looking flawless, even, and natural looking. Exfoliation can also make the skin appear fresher and younger. During your break from the tan, you should moisturise your body with an ultra rich moisturiser such as the Body Shop Shea Butter. Focus on your dehydrated areas, or any problem areas where the tan tends to gather. My problem areas would be the backs of my knees, my elbows, under my arms, in between my boobs and around my feet. Trust me, exfoliating and moisturising in the weeks and days before your spray tan will make a huge difference to the result you get.

If you want a truly perfect fake tan to develop, then your skin needs to be hydrated from the inside, so start increasing your daily intake of water. Hydrated skin will absorb the tan much better, thus causing it to develop properly, not to mention make it last longer!

DO

Do stop using fake tan (the developing kind) for two weeks prior to your holiday. The condition of your skin prior to the application is so important. If, however, you have been wearing fake tan, it can leave your skin a little dehydrated, which can impact hugely on your new tan. This is why I always stop wearing fake tans for around 2-3 weeks prior to my holiday. That way, my skin is a perfect blank canvass for the new tan. If you need a dash of colour during your break from tan, then just use the good old-fashioned instant tan. I love the instant tans by Rimmel and Karora.

Problem solved!

KEEP CALM AND GET A TAN

DO

Whenever I am wearing a tan, I will always moisturise my body from head to toe with a really good moisturiser, so as to lock in the tan. I will also apply a small amount of instant tan over my colour just to give it that extra glow. I absolutely love the Karora Instant Tan because it has a golden hue that makes your skin look so radiant.

DO

Do know the shade that suits you! I have tried literally every spray tan on the market, so it pretty much goes without saying that I know for sure what I like and what I don't like! I love tans that produce a dark golden colour, because I find they give off a nice natural glow. For some reason, they also tend to wear off the best. The fake tan I always opt for is Lauren's Way (LW). The LW fake tan is, in my opinion, the ultimate tanning lotion for acquiring that natural golden holiday glow. I find it always gives me perfectly bronzed tan. It is such a warm colour and it doesn't streak or go orange either! If you are having a tan applied for a holiday, then I would recommend getting a spray tan done around 24 hours before your flight. Always make sure you go to a good spray tan technician. I love going to Olivia in Allure Beauty, Drumcondra.

My Top Five Tans

Lauren's Way Tan (Darker than dark mousse)

Baby B Browne Tan (Medium)

Vita Liberata (Mousse medium)

he-shi Rapid One Hour Tan

When it comes to instant tans, Rimmel's Sunshimmer Instant Tan BB Cream is definitely one worth checking out. The sun kissed glow it gives is just fab.

I am often asked where I go to get my hair taken care of. Well for my hair extensions, I always go to Valerie in Cowboys & Angels on Dublin's South William Street. When it comes to blow-dries, I go to Jane in Red Velvet Hair Salon in Ballyboughal, Dublin. She's amazing at creating big hair! If I can't make it into the salon however, then I go straight to Ami McPartlin in my hometown of Skerries. She's such

a brilliant stylist and even did my hair for the book photo shoot! Of course, I don't always have these wonderful professionals by my side, so over the years, I developed my own set of hair styling skills. As I receive so many messages from readers requesting tutorials on the various hairstyles I have donned, I decided to feature here the three styles I am asked about most!

Hair Tutorials

Tutorial – High Ponytail

First, I backcomb the top section of my hair and then I add some OSIS Dust It Powder. I then grab all the hair and pull it up at the crown, before tying it tightly with a hair bobbin.

I then pull some strands of hair from the hair bobbin so that the style is not too sleek, and I always clip up any little hairs that might be falling at the back.

To finish off the style, I brush through the pony and mist it with hairspray.

Tutorial – Side Plait

I have always loved the side plait hairstyle, and even wore my hair that way for the L'Oreal Colour Trophy Awards last year.

The side plait is the LBD of hair, i.e. a total classic. It's so pretty and feminine but yet stylish and versatile. I mean, you can literally wear this style anywhere. Kim Kardashian is just one of many celebs who have worn this style both on the red carpet and when at the gym! You don't even need to be precise with the styling if you don't wish, because a messy side plait is just as beautiful!

This kind of hairstyle doesn't really work on freshly washed tresses, so if you're finding it difficult to style, then just spritz some dry shampoo throughout the hair, or maybe add some OSIS Dust It Powder for texture.

If you want to create some height at the crown of the head, lightly backcomb the roots, and then hold it in place with some hairspray.

Next, pull the hair to one side, and gently tease the strands with a comb or a backcombing brush. This will help with the 'messiness' of the look.

If you need help keeping the hair in place, tie your hair into a side ponytail and just remove the hair tie once the plait is secured in place. Once you have finished plaiting the hair and have it secured the end of it with a hair tie, you can start very lightly teasing the hair out of place, but only do this if you think it's not already 'messy' enough.

Tutorial – High Volume

Whenever I want to inject some bouncy volume into my hair, I follow a simple process and it never fails me.

I always section off my hair first, before then backcombing each section.

1   A good backcombing brush is essential for creating volume, and you can easily pick one up in any pharmacy or salon supply shop. Backcombing does not involve vigorously brushing the hair back and forth. So many girls do this, but it's a big mistake because it will end up breaking your hair. The best way to backcomb is to hold up a section of the hair, place the brush in the middle of the section, and bring the brush down to the root in one straight line. Go back to the middle again and bring the brush down a second time if necessary. I like to focus on backcombing the crown in particular.

2   Once each section has been backcombed, I sprinkle on some OSIS Dust It Powder. This helps add texture as well as set the backcombed hair. Some people do find OSIS a bit difficult to use because it sets quite fast, so if you don't want to use this, then instead you can spritz the backcombed hair with a strong hairspray. Batiste also has a volumising powder that is quite good and not as quick setting as OSIS.

3   Afterwards, I lightly brush the backcombed sections down with a paddle brush. This gives your hair a far more natural voluminous look.

4   I then part my fringe and style it to suit.

5   Following this, I add one final dusting of OSIS, and then mist my hair with either L'Oreal Infinity Hairspray, or Elemis Hairspray. I really like these hairsprays because they don't leave a sticky residue in my hair.

My Make-Up Must Haves

Lippy, liner, powder, primer... what does your little heart desire?

....
....
....
....
....
....
....
....
....
....
....
....
....
....
....
....
....
....
....
....
....

Chapter Ten

Fashion Week, Frappés and Fun:
#SoSueMeGoesToNYC

Paparazzi. Vintage stores. New York Fashion Week. Amazing food. Big blow-dries. Fab cocktails. Manicure bars. Breakfast bars. Dashing in and out of yellow taxis. Dining out every night. Photo shoots in Times Square. Guest list only parties. Being in a club with Paris and Nicky Hilton... New York, you have exhausted me, but I am ridiculously in love with you!

ANYONE WHO KNOWS me knows that I'm a total home bird, but I honestly think I would move to New York first thing in the morning if the opportunity presented itself! It is the most amazing place on earth, and after having experienced a slice of NY life, I can now completely understand why people say it's like a totally different world. In fact, I doubt any other city in the world can rival that indescribable vibe you get when you're in New York. The city was everything I expected it to be. There's just something so magical about it, especially in the evenings as the sun is going down and those famous city lights are coming on.

How It All Happened!

I mentioned in my 2014 goals earlier in the book that visiting New York was something I really wanted to do this year as I had never been there. At the time, I had no idea that this book would be happening or that I would get the chance to attend New York Fashion Week. When the opportunity came along, no way could I turn it down!

In my opinion, New York is the fashion capital of the world, it's the home of one of my all-time favourite TV shows, *Sex and the City*, and what better place to write an exciting fashion chapter for my book?

I was so happy that Dylan was able to travel with me and during our time there we got to attend catwalk shows, visit all the sights such as the Empire State Building and Ground Zero, go to a Broadway show and of course do some shopping! I even got to spend time with some family. Over the following chapter I have documented each day of my trip – my time at New York Fashion Week, the clothes, the celeb sightings, the tours and everything in between! Organising a big trip like NYC is a job in itself so I've also included all my secrets and tips for planning your trip and what to do when you get there. New York is an amazing city so if you get the chance to go there, I say go for it!

SoSueMe Secret

If you are thinking about travelling to NYC, I would highly recommend you get in touch with Tour America about your trips and tours. We got some seriously amazing package deals from them.

WELCOME!

THE STATUE OF LIBERTY
NATIONAL MONUMENT & ELLIS ISLAND

P11021104602158865

Battery Park Flex

VALID FOR
One Admission,
Within 3 days of 09/15/2014
Enjoy your Visit!

TRIP & TOURS
STATUE OF LIBERTY-GROUNDS ONLY
NY Adult CityPass Redemption

VISITORS
Price $0.00
---Ferry:$4.00
---Audio:$4.00
$4 Audio Tour Portion Includes Sales Tax
157400 09/15/2014 12:34 PM 33 Order ID:

2014/2015
NEW YORK
CityPASS
Valid 9 Days
Beginning

Disney
Aladdín
"THE NEW DISNEY BLOCKBUSTER!"
ASSOCIATED PRESS

MARC JACOBS

WOMEN'S COLLECTION
SPRING 2015

THURSDAY SEPTEMBER 11 6:00 PM

PARK AVENUE ARMORY
643 PARK AVENUE

K SECTION **2** ROW **3** SEAT

RSVP 212 590 0413 HTTP://FASHIONSPS.COM/KCD
THIS INVITATION IS NON-TRANSFERABLE
PHOTO ID WILL BE REQUIRED FOR ADMITTANCE

RALPH LAUREN
Collection

Spring 2015

Skylight Clarkson Sq
560 Washington Street

Please enter at Gate 26E between
Houston & Spring Streets

Thursday, September 11, 2014
10:00 am

F Section **4** Row **J** Seat

Please present this card for admission

---

on location tours
Sex and the City Hotspots

Follow in the footsteps of
Carrie & Co. as you visit locations
from the popular TV show and movies.

913-9780 • www.onlocationtours.com

CONFIRMED
JACKSON/SUZANNEMS

DELTA
ETKT 1 006 5233850468 6 HOPKHR
SEAT REQUEST

FLIGHT DL91 DATE 09SEP DEPARTS 1115A
DUBLIN
NYC-KENNEDY
OPERATED BY DELTA AIR LINES INC.
SEAT ASSIGNED AT GATE

DOCS-OK DUB117 36E

New York Diary:  Day 1

We were on our way to meet with one of Dylan's friends, Jack, when I spotted a vintage shop on East 9th street called Cobblestones.

It was a tiny shop that looked like something from the 70s, but it had a real New York feel to it. I ended up calling into that shop every single day! The store owner was always placing new stock on the shelves so you were guaranteed to spot something different each time you went in. I bought three hats there, one of which was a vintage Givenchy hat that I wore to Fashion Week. I came to think of Cobblestones as my own little secret style haunt, but I later discovered that it was in fact renowned for its celebrity fan base, and that quite a number of A-listers travel there in search of vintage treasures. So much for it being secret!

Later that evening, we headed into Macy's. Guys, that place is seriously unreal. I'm just thankful it's not in Ireland, otherwise I would be absolutely bankrupt! Macy's was where I pretty much found shopping nirvana, (not to mention the most fab pair of Steve Madden heels!)

SoSueMe Secret

Don't spend a fortune on hotels or apartments. You won't even be in your accommodation that often, because you will be out doing touristy things. We found our apartment on the AirBnB website, which is a wonderful way of sourcing great accommodation that's not expensive.

New York Diary: Day 2

I got up early and hopped into the Hair Lounge on East 9th Street to book my appointment for 11am so that I would be ready in time for the first fashion show, WantMyLook. A great guy called Roney was my hair stylist. He was just so good at washing and styling my extensions that I ended up going to the Hair Lounge every second day for my big New York blow-dry!

The outfit I chose for the WantMyLook show was very vintage inspired. The general theme of any fashion week is effortless chic, so I chose a really cool vintage red leather skirt and a re-worked leather jacket from 9 Crow Street, which is, in my opinion, 100% the best vintage shop in Dublin. I then paired it with a statement t-shirt from River Island. The leather jacket, which I had draped over my shoulders, had the most unbelievable red lining inside so the whole look was very Louboutin inspired!

When we arrived at Metropolitan West for the WantMyLook fashion show, there was a queue as long as Grafton Street, but everyone in it was dressed to kill, so I could have happily stayed outside just looking at all the style! There was so much press there too. Bravo TV, lots of street style photographers, fashion journalists … it was just manic. When we arrived at the door, the guy in charge of the guest list started chatting to us, and when he realised we were Irish, he gave us front row tickets. I couldn't believe our luck! Front row tickets are like gold dust. The show was amazing. Literally hundreds of photographers were standing at the end of the runway snapping anything that moved.

I was seriously excited about this particular fashion show because Lilly Ghalichi, the owner of the WantMyLook fashion website, is a huge TV star in America and a total idol of mine. It was so weird seeing her on stage, because I have been following her on Instagram for the past two years and I am absolutely obsessed with her. She's so business-minded; a real go-getting ambitious entrepreneur. She has her own swimwear line, a fashion website, a range of false lashes, and a diamond jewellery collection. Lilly is definitely someone I would have huge admiration for. At one point, while she was on the runway in front of me, she even smiled directly at me. Star-struck is not the word! I thought my all time high point was meeting and interviewing Marc Jacobs last year, but I was so wrong! Seeing Lilly up close was definitely the ultimate experience for this fashion blogger.

Later that evening, Dylan and I went out for some cocktails and dinner before heading to a fashion week after-party hosted by OK Magazine and Boohoo.com in the VIP Rooms. We were there as guests of Boohoo.com.

While Dylan and I were queuing for the party, I noticed there was a camera crew nearby, so I assumed it was another red carpet job. The girl queuing in front of us also seemed to be talking to the camera every now and then.

While we were waiting for our line to move, I got on the phone to Retro Flame blogger Erica Fox, because we had arranged to meet inside the club. After I got off the phone, a woman approached me and asked me to sign a waiver. When I asked her why, she explained that I had been standing behind the singer Christina Milian, who was there filming her reality TV show. I was in the shot with her, so they needed my permission. I was shocked. I hadn't even realised that the girl in front of me was Christina Milian! That's the great thing about New York, you never know who you will bump into.

Sitting next to Paris and Nicky Hilton

The party had a very strict guest list and there were so many celebrities floating about. Nicky Hilton was there launching her book and her sister Paris was with her. They were surrounded by really heavy security, but our table was right next to theirs, so we ended up sitting about two feet away from them, which was pretty surreal.

In the club, I met with Erica and her sister. Erica has just moved to NY for the year and was working at fashion week, so she filled me in on all the backstage news. It was great to see a familiar face because it can be quite overwhelming to be in such a huge city.

Dylan and I left the party at around 1am to get an early night. We had the Ralph Lauren show at 10am the following morning, but I had to get up at 7am to reply to emails, and to work on both my book and blog posts. I was meant to be in New York for all of fashion week, but due to book commitments, I had to push my trip back, so I attended the final two days of it instead. I really hope to attend the whole thing next year. I also have Milan Fashion Week in my line of sight! The hardcore fashion peeps fly straight from New York Fashion Week to Milan Fashion Week, and next year, I really hope to be joining them!

New York Diary:  Day 3

On Thursday, the final day of NYFW, we were scheduled to attend three shows: Ralph Lauren at 10am, Dorin Negrau at midday, and Marc Jacobs at 6pm. The Dorin Negrau show was on in the Lincoln Centre, the nerve centre of fashion week.

The energy and atmosphere at that particular spot was unbelievable! There are countless paparazzi and street style photographers roaming about. I also spotted a number of international bloggers and their photographers taking pictures outside the iconic building. Honestly guys, it was just so cool! Dorin Negrau's show itself was not to everyone's taste, but still amazing to experience. The room in which the show was taking place was absolutely enormous, and had a kind of warehouse feel to it. The mood of this show was of a very dark nature, and had lots of heavy rock music. I think it was inspired by Dracula.

Once a show is over, people rush straight to the next show. There's no such thing as hanging around and having the craic. The shows take place in different venues all over the city, so you can't afford to waste time once a show closes. It's straight into a taxi and on to the next venue. The thing about New York is that everywhere is within 15 minutes of you, but because the traffic is so crazy, it takes at least half an hour to get to where you want to go. This definitely does not suit someone like me who is always chronically late! For fashion week, I really had to take myself in hand, because if you are even five minutes late for a show, you're not allowed in. The rules are so strict, so I was lucky I had Dylan with me to make sure I didn't delay anywhere! I was jotting down so many notes for my book and blog that I often lost track of time!

Our final show was Marc Jacobs, and so for that, I decided to debut my newly purchased green Givenchy hat.

I was photographed non-stop in that outfit! The fashion photographers loved it. When I turned up at the venue, different paparazzi guys were screaming over at me, all calling me to stand for various pictures. The show organisers actually had to move me on from the photographers so that I could get to my seat before the show began. It was the most bizarre, albeit brilliant, experience ever! On that note, if you ever go to fashion week, make sure you are always camera-ready, because if the show you're attending is a busy one, then it's quite likely you will be papped by the street style photographers.

Anyway, for the Marc Jacobs show, we were in the second row, which I was absolutely thrilled about because this show was a huge deal. I had heard Kendall Jenner was going to be walking the runway, and as I am a big fan of the Kardashians, I was so excited by the prospect of seeing her. Granted, all the models had a uniform of zero makeup and black choppy wigs, but I was still able to spot Kendall.

Even though I was only there for two days of fashion week, I was wrecked! A week would exhaust you if you weren't prepared for it. I had two shows on Wednesday and three on Thursday, and between all the travelling, the changing, and the rushing, it does wear you out! That said, I absolutely buzzed off the whole event. There is something so special about that moment when the lights drop to pitch black, the music starts pumping, then the spotlights are suddenly turned on, and the first model walks out on to the runway. The hairs just stand on the back of your neck.

New York Diary:

Friday was spent shopping, enjoying cocktails, and having a look around the village where we were staying. I also spent a couple of hours in Starbucks working on this very chapter! That night, Dylan and I headed to The Staunton Social for a big night out with Dyl's friends. The Staunton Social is a fab tapas bar with food to die for, and RnB music pumping through the speakers. People would arrive in at 2am in the morning and still get served food! The concept of a closing time never quite made it to New York!

New York Diary: Day 5

The next day, we went to Central Park to shoot some looks for the book. The park is beautiful, and so peaceful too. It was just perfect for our shoot. When I set off for New York, I was determined to get street shots, but it's such a busy city that it can often be difficult to get the right picture without the risk of being run over by a cab!

That night, Dylan and I went to Gyu-Kaku, a Japanese barbeque restaurant in Manhattan, where you cook your own food! The restaurant itself was amazing, with its large glass windows looking out onto the city.

New York Diary:  Day 6

On Sunday, we went to the Empire State building, which is definitely one of the most incredible landmarks in New York. My favourite part of our trip to the Empire State was that moment we stepped out of the elevator and saw that spectacular view of New York. It was like looking down on the city from the sky.

SoSueMe Secret

We got the New York City Pass from Tour America, which is a booklet that contains tickets for different tourist locations. It costs around $100, and trust me, it's more than worth it, because you will get totally ripped off if you buy the tickets in the city itself.

New York Diary:  Day 7

On Monday, we decided to take a trip out to the Statue of Liberty. We also took the tour around it, and listened to really interesting information about the statue through headphones while we walked.

After a trip to Ellis island, we then headed back to East village to take some street style pictures for the book.

The most amazing view ever!

New York Diary:

Tuesday was a particularly busy day, but a hugely exciting one too thanks to a certain Sex and the City tour! During the tour, they bring you to all the locations, like the restaurant where Carrie and Mr Big had their rehearsal dinner, the café where the four ladies often had lunch, the park where Miranda and Steve got married, and the Tiffany's where Charlotte was proposed to. We even got to enjoy some cocktails in Steve's bar, Scout. During the tour, we were also let off to do some shopping in the same places frequented by the four ladies.

What I really liked about the tour was how they played specific clips from SATC so that we could watch the scenes that had been filmed at the locations we were about to visit. Even if you had forgotten certain parts of the series or the movies, the clips helped jog the memory. Unfortunately, Carrie's apartment building is no longer part of the tour. The apartment interior is filmed in a studio, but the building itself is a privately owned property, so the tour can no longer bring tourists there to pose for photos on the famous steps. I, however, was determined to see Carrie's building, so I emailed a New Yorker friend of mine and asked her for the address. Ladies, if you go to NY and you want to see Carrie's block, it's on 66 Perry Street (Between Bleecker and West 4th)! As soon as I had the address, Dylan and I hailed a cab and went straight there. It was amazing to see the actual location, but I couldn't get a photo on the steps as there was a lot of renovation work taking place outside.

On the balcony above where Carrie and Mr Big had their rehearsal dinner

The long table where Carrie and Mr Big had their rehearsal dinner

on location tours

Sex and the City Hotspots

Overall, it was a really cool tour, and definitely one worth taking, especially if you are with your best friends, but my advice is not to get your hopes up too high about it. Even though it's a great experience for the die-hard SATC fan, it was also pretty strict in some ways. You are only allowed out of the bus for some of the locations, but not all. For instance, when we were brought to the small park where Miranda and Steve got married, we were not allowed to get out and walk around it. The reason for this is because it's actually a children's playground, and only parents are allowed entry. Due to it being a children's play area, this meant that photos of the park were also forbidden. That said, I would still recommend the tour. It was a fab experience and if you're a huge fan like me, you will love it.

SoSueMe Secret

If you are going to NY and you want to take the SATC tour, make sure you buy your tour tickets from a good travel agent before you go to NY, otherwise you will get majorly ripped off if you buy them when you get out there.

The next stop on our New York trip was the Jovani showrooms to meet the CEO, Abraham Maslavi. Jovani is a very beautiful label, and Cari's Closet is the exclusive Irish stockist of the brand. My meeting with Abraham came about after Lisa Duffy, the owner of Cari's Closet, told him about SoSueMe.ie. When she told him I was going to be in New York, a meeting was arranged, which I was so excited about. The Jovani HQ is located on Broadway 36th and 37th, which is a very cool part of New York City, and when Dylan and I walked through the showrooms, we were actually gobsmacked. Seriously guys, you should have seen this place, it was DRESS HEAVEN! The whole place was laid out so glamorously, and even Dylan was like *"holy shit this place is incredible!"*

The showrooms are where the fashion buyers come in to view the dresses and place their orders. If certain dresses catch a buyer's interest, then the stunning in-house models will try them on so that the buyer can see exactly how each item looks and fits. There is also an array of fine wines and sushi all laid out for the buyers to enjoy while they view the clothes. They are wined and dined while they spend hours selecting which dresses to buy. Now *that's* a dream job!

Abraham was such a gentleman, and so lovely to talk to. He gave me free rein to look around his amazing showroom and he also invited me to the Jovani fashion shows. To have met with the main name over a fashion powerhouse was amazing from a business and networking point of view.

After we left Jovani, we went for a bite to eat and then on to a Broadway show. I was determined to see Aladdin on Broadway because it had always been my favourite Disney film. Even when I was a kid, I always wanted to be Princess Jasmine! We were so lucky with our tickets. We had been queuing up to buy them, when a lady announced that all tickets had been sold out. Naturally, the rest of the queue began to disperse, but I just had an inkling that our luck would turn, so I told Dyl to hang on a bit. Sure enough, five minutes before the show began, it was announced that two tickets had become available due to a cancellation. Our luck had indeed come in! The show itself was so amazing, and we were both lost for words by the end of it.

Disney
Aladdin

"THE NEW DISNEY
BLOCKBUSTER!"

New York Diary:  Day 9

Wednesday was dedicated to shooting the book cover on Fifth Avenue. I have to admit I was getting seriously homesick at that stage. In fact, that night, when we were out having dinner, Dylan mentioned something about Coco and Harper and I just burst into tears! I honestly think the other restaurant guests thought he was breaking up with me!

I phoned my mum for a chat and when I told her I was feeling a little homesick, she suggested I pay a visit to my granduncle Frank and my cousins in New Jersey.

Straight away, I got in touch with Frank and we arranged a big family get together. A limo arrived to take myself and Dyl to New Jersey where we met with my cousins at Frank's pub. It was so nice to spend some time with the extended family and to just enjoy a few laughs and stories over dinner and drinks.

With my grand-uncle Frank

Despite the homesickness I felt towards the end of the trip, I would still love to live in New York, or even somewhere like L.A. or Miami, though if I did move, I have no doubt that I would have my family plagued with Skype calls!

New York Diary:

As Thursday was our last day in the big city, we decided to get up early and pack in as many things as possible. First we did a little shopping and picked up some gifts for family and friends. I also couldn't leave the fashion capital without paying one final visit to the shrines of style and beauty, so I made straight for Marc Jacobs, Tiffanys, Macy's, Sephora, and Michael Kors!

Afterwards, we went to Ground Zero. That was a tough trip; very harrowing. After we had asked a cab driver to take us there, he started telling us about what it was like to have been in the city on September 11th. He recalled how for miles, buildings and people were covered in dust after the collapse of the towers. He said that in all his years living in New York, that was the only time he ever saw the city come to a complete standstill. Just hearing his recollection of that day made the hairs on the back of my neck stand, but that was nothing compared to impact the location itself had on me.

Before I go any further, let me just say that an average day in New York is on a level of crazy that would be similar to a Saturday night in Dublin after the Dubs have won the All-Ireland. In the middle of all this madness however, is the most beautifully serene and peaceful area you could possibly imagine. Ground Zero. Some people pray there, others walk around in silence, but the only sound you can hear is that of the two massive waterfalls that now mark the place where the two towers once stood.

The name of each victim is etched into marble, and the whole site is a most beautiful tribute to those who perished there that day. In one way, it's a very surreal experience because it's almost hard to believe that this beacon of tranquility was once the site of a major atrocity. There is just no way you could walk through it and not be moved to tears.

The 9/11 museum is not for the faint heated. In there, they have everything from fire trucks, to the remnants of luggage from the planes that were flown into the towers. They also have recordings of the voicemails that were left by passengers on the planes. I cried listening to them. It was so heartbreaking to hear them say goodbye to their families. I especially found it very difficult to see the luggage items, particularly the kids shoes. The museum also had things like pictures and calendars from the towers offices, and even the stairway that the survivors ran down. Even the steel piping from where the plane first made impact was on display, as were the window frames from both planes, and parts of a trolley used by an air hostess on one of the flights. Throughout the museum, videos of news bulletins from September 11th played continuously, which in itself was heartbreaking to watch. You could see the news stations suddenly stop and break to a news flash; the newsreaders visibly panic-stricken by the news they were delivering.

If you ever visit that museum, the first piece of advice I would offer is to go in prepared, because it will affect you emotionally. Secondly, do not visit it on the same day you are due to board a plane. This is especially the case if you are a very nervous flyer like I am! Myself and Dylan made the big mistake of visiting the Ground Zero museum right before we had to leave for the airport, and I was definitely not the better of it. What you see in the museum is very hard-hitting, and like I said, not at all for the faint-hearted.

After our visit to the site, we went back to our apartment, grabbed our suitcases and said goodbye to the greatest city on earth. When we arrived home, I was meant to then board a flight to London for London Fashion Week, but I was so exhausted that I just couldn't face another flight, let alone another event.

NYC is definitely my favourite place and I can't wait to go back there.

Despite the touch of homesickness, I genuinely would LOVE to live there. By the end of our trip, I had really developed my own little routine. Every morning, I would get up early, throw on some cute shorts and a t-shirt, and go for a brisk walk around the village where we were staying. I would then meet Dylan for breakfast at a lovely Ukrainian restaurant where they made the best omelettes and had the nicest breakfast tea. Afterwards, I would return to the apartment, blog, reply to emails, and get ready for the day ahead. I think I kind of felt like I was living there because we were staying in an apartment rather than a hotel.

Living in NYC would be the dream, but I don't think I will allow it remain as a dream for long. In fact, come January I might even be including it on my list of goals for 2015. After all, who knows what next year will bring?

Places To Go

Travel broadens the mind... and empties the wallet! But seriously, it's good to go to new places, see a bit of the world and be filled with new ideas. Is there somewhere that you've always wanted to see? It could be as close as Carlow or as far-flung as Florida, any new place can be full of hidden gems and leave you feeling refreshed. Time to start making plans, one city at a time.